GCSE AQA
Additional Science
Higher Workbook

This book is for anyone doing **GCSE AQA Additional Science** at higher level.
It covers everything you'll need for your year 11 exams.

It's full of **tricky questions**... each one designed to make you **sweat**
— because that's the only way you'll get any **better**.

There are questions to see **what facts** you know. There are questions
to see how well you can **apply those facts**. And there are questions
to see what you know about **how science works**.

It's also got some daft bits in to try and make the whole
experience at least vaguely entertaining for you.

What CGP is all about

Our sole aim here at CGP is to produce the highest
quality books — carefully written, immaculately presented
and dangerously close to being funny.

Then we work our socks off to get them
out to you — at the cheapest possible prices.

Contents

CHEMISTRY 2B — REACTION RATES, SALTS AND ELECTROLYSIS

PHYSICS 2A — FORCES AND THEIR EFFECTS

PHYSICS 2B — ELECTRICITY AND THE ATOM

Published by CGP

Editors:
Charlotte Burrows, Katherine Craig, Mary Falkner, Helena Hayes, Felicity Inkpen,
Rosie McCurrie, Jane Sawers, Sarah Williams.

Contributors:
Steve Coggins, Mike Dagless, Jane Davies, Ian H Davis, Max Fishel, James Foster,
Dr Giles R Greenway, Frederick Langridge, Dr Iona M J Hamilton, Rebecca Harvey,
John Myers, Sidney Stringer Community School.

ISBN: 978 1 84762 763 6

With thanks to Helen Brace, Mark A Edwards, Mary Falkner, David Hickinson, Peter Schofield
and Karen Wells for the proofreading.
With thanks to Jan Greenway, Laura Jakubowski and Laura Stoney for the copyright research.

Groovy website: www.cgpbooks.co.uk

Printed by Elanders Ltd, Newcastle upon Tyne.
Jolly bits of clipart from CorelDRAW®

Based on the classic CGP style created by Richard Parsons.

Cells

Q1 Plant and animal cells have **similarities** and **differences**.
Complete each statement below by choosing the correct words.

a) **Plant** / **animal** cells, but not **plant** / **animal** cells, contain chloroplasts.

b) Plant cells and algal cells have a **vacuole** / **cell wall**, which is made of cellulose.

c) **Both plant and animal cells** / **only animal cells** contain ribosomes, which is where
carbohydrates / **proteins** are made in the cell.

d) The cell **wall** / **membrane** holds the cell together and controls what goes in and out.

Q2 State what the following cell structures **contain** or are **made of** and what their **functions** are.

a) The **nucleus** contains ....

Its function is ....

b) **Chloroplasts** contain ....

Their function is ....

c) The **cell wall** is made of ....

Its function is ....

Q3 **Mitochondria** are very important cellular structures.

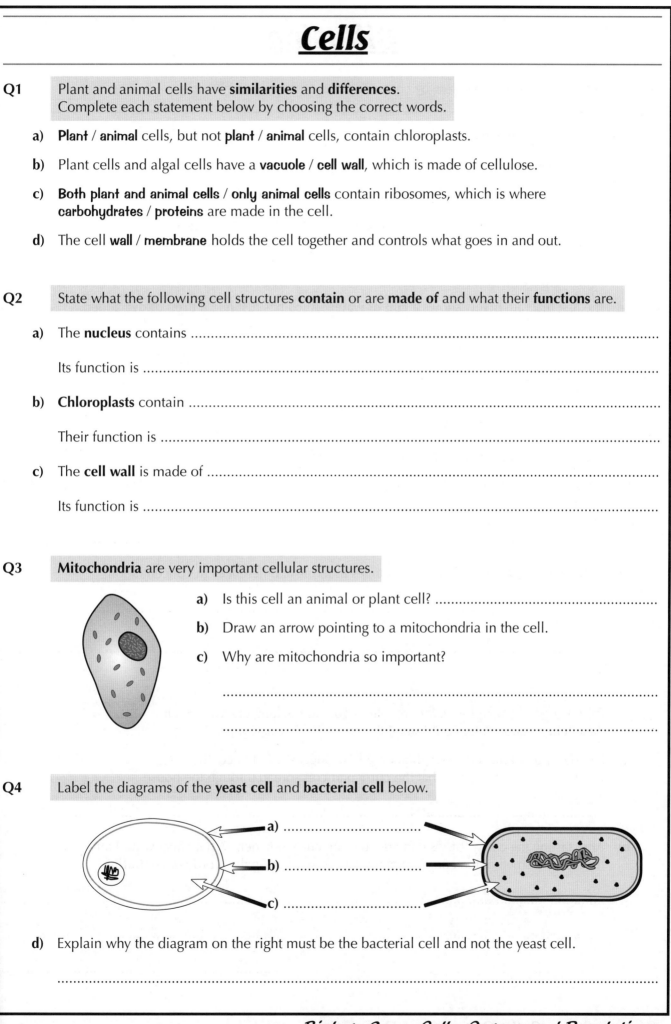

a) Is this cell an animal or plant cell? ....

b) Draw an arrow pointing to a mitochondria in the cell.

c) Why are mitochondria so important?

....

....

Q4 Label the diagrams of the **yeast cell** and **bacterial cell** below.

a) ....

b) ....

c) ....

d) Explain why the diagram on the right must be the bacterial cell and not the yeast cell.

....

Diffusion

Q1   Complete the passage below by choosing the most appropriate words.

> Diffusion is the **direct** / **random** movement of particles from an area where they are at a
>
> **higher** / **lower** concentration to an area where they are at a **higher** / **lower** concentration.
>
> There is a **net** / **rod** movement of particles from that area. The rate of diffusion is faster
>
> when the concentration gradient is **bigger** / **smaller** and in **liquids** / **gases**.

Q2   The first diagram below shows a **cup of water** which has just had a **drop of dye** added.

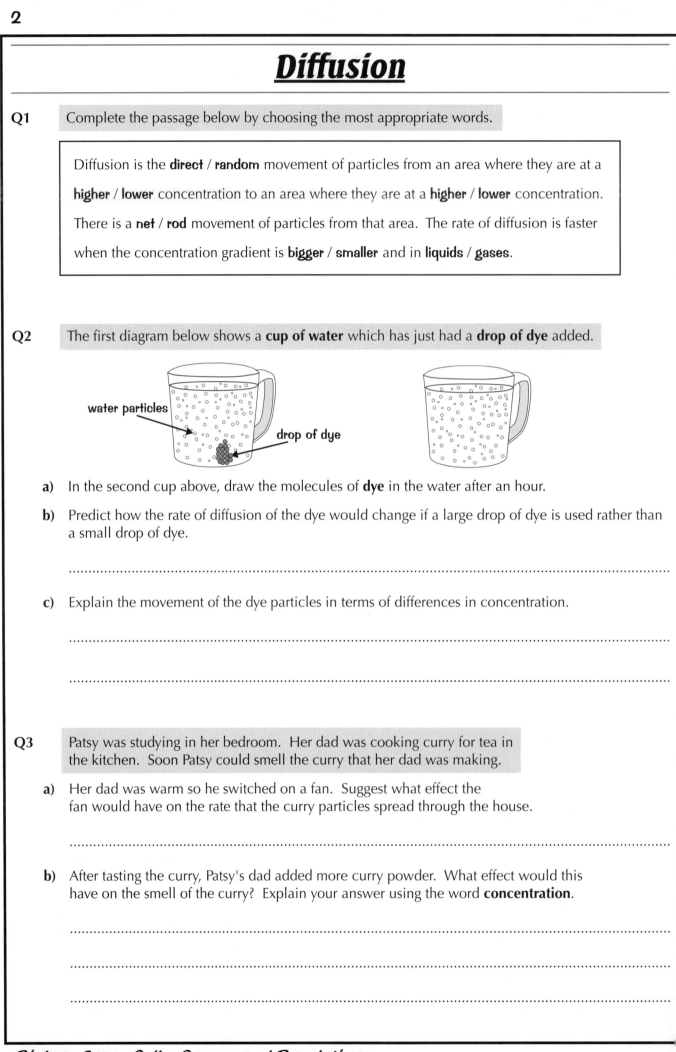

water particles

drop of dye

a)   In the second cup above, draw the molecules of **dye** in the water after an hour.

b)   Predict how the rate of diffusion of the dye would change if a large drop of dye is used rather than
a small drop of dye.

....

c)   Explain the movement of the dye particles in terms of differences in concentration.

....

....

Q3   Patsy was studying in her bedroom. Her dad was cooking curry for tea in
the kitchen. Soon Patsy could smell the curry that her dad was making.

a)   Her dad was warm so he switched on a fan. Suggest what effect the
fan would have on the rate that the curry particles spread through the house.

....

b)   After tasting the curry, Patsy's dad added more curry powder. What effect would this
have on the smell of the curry? Explain your answer using the word **concentration**.

....

....

....

Diffusion

Q4 Some statements about **diffusion** are written below.
Decide which are correct and then write **true** or **false** in the spaces.

a) Diffusion takes place in all types of substances. ....

b) Diffusion is usually quicker in liquids than in gases. ....

c) Diffusion happens more quickly when there is a higher concentration gradient. ....

d) Dissolved substances can move in and out of cells by diffusion. ....

e) Oxygen molecules are too large to diffuse through cell membranes. ....

Q5 Two models of diffusion are shown below.

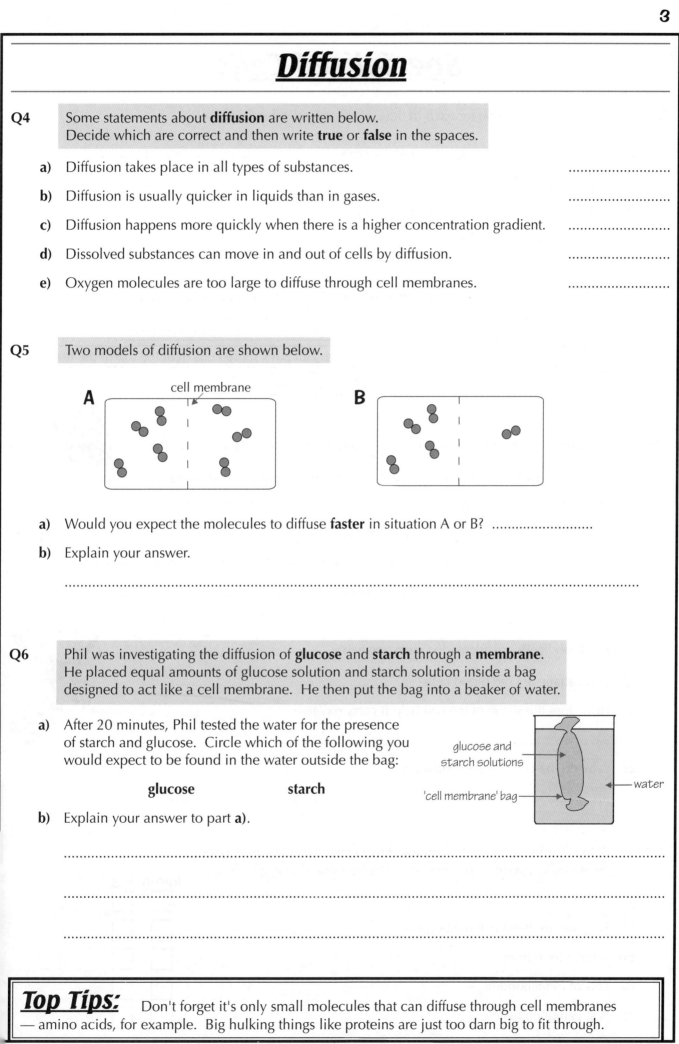

a) Would you expect the molecules to diffuse **faster** in situation A or B? ....

b) Explain your answer.

....

Q6 Phil was investigating the diffusion of **glucose** and **starch** through a **membrane**.
He placed equal amounts of glucose solution and starch solution inside a bag
designed to act like a cell membrane. He then put the bag into a beaker of water.

a) After 20 minutes, Phil tested the water for the presence
of starch and glucose. Circle which of the following you
would expect to be found in the water outside the bag:

glucose   **starch**

b) Explain your answer to part **a)**.

....

....

....

Top Tips: Don't forget it's only small molecules that can diffuse through cell membranes
— amino acids, for example. Big hulking things like proteins are just too darn big to fit through.

4

Specialised Cells

Q1   Give the correct name for each of the specialised cells described below.

a)   These cells transport oxygen around the body.   ....

b)   The male reproductive cell.   ....

c)   Cells that open and close stomata on leaves.   ....

d)   The female reproductive cell.   ....

Q2   Below are three features of **palisade leaf cells**. Draw lines to match each feature to its function.

Lots of chloroplasts		gives a large surface area for absorbing CO_2
Tall shape		means you can pack more cells in at the top of the leaf
Thin shape		for photosynthesis

Q3   Complete the following paragraph about **guard cells**, using the words below.

night   turgid   flaccid   photosynthesis   stomata

Guard cells open and close the .... When the plant has lots of water the

guard cells are .... This makes the stomata open, so gases can be exchanged for

.... When the plant is short of water the guard cells become

................................., making the stomata close. They also close at .... to save water.

Q4   Red blood cells are adapted to **carry oxygen**.

a)   What **shape** are red blood cells?   ....

b)   How does the shape of the cell help it carry oxygen?

....

c)   Why do the cells have **no nucleus**?

....

Q5   Below is a list of features of **reproductive cells**. Decide which ones are found in **sperm** cells and which ones are found in **egg** cells.

Sperm   Egg

a)   A long tail   ☐   ☐

b)   Enzymes to digest cell membranes   ☐   ☐

c)   A large food reserve   ☐   ☐

d)   Lots of mitochondria   ☐   ☐

e)   A streamlined head   ☐   ☐

Cell Organisation

Q1 Sort the following list by writing each term in the correct place in the table below.

sperm	blood	digestive system	snail
cat	liver	egg (human)	stomach
reproductive system	muscle	eye	dog
excretory system	white blood cell	heart	small intestine

Cell	Tissue	Organ	Organ system	Organism

Q2 Tick the boxes to show whether the following statements are **true** or **false**.

		True	False
a)	The liver produces bile.	☐	☐
b)	Organisms have only one organ system.	☐	☐
c)	Glandular tissue produces substances including enzymes.	☐	☐
d)	A heart contains different types of tissue.	☐	☐
e)	The inside of the gut is covered by epithelial tissue.	☐	☐
f)	An epithelial cell is approximately 0.1 cm long.	☐	☐
g)	The stomach is over 1000 times longer than an epithelial cell.	☐	☐

Q3 Put the words below in the correct order to fill in the boxes showing how cells in the digestive system are organised.

stomach

human

epithelial cells

epithelial tissue

↓
↓
↓
digestive system
↓

Cell Organisation

Q4 The **digestive system** is an organ system, made up of tissues and organs.

a) Complete the passage by choosing the most appropriate words from the list below.

muscular tissue	churn	liver	nutrients
bile	materials	organs	tissues

The digestive system exchanges .... with the environment

by taking in .... and releasing substances, such as

.... The digestive system is made up of ....,

like the stomach and the .... The stomach is made up of various

different ...., for example ....,

which moves the stomach wall to .... up the food.

b) Describe the job of the glandular tissue in the stomach.

....

c) Name **two** glands in the digestive system.

....

Q5 Large multicellular organisms develop **organs systems**. During development, cells **differentiate**.

a) Explain the purpose of organs systems in large multicellular organisms.

....

b) Define the term 'differentiation'.

....

....

Q6 Define the following terms:

a) a tissue

....

b) an organ

....

c) an organ system

....

Plant Structure and Photosynthesis

Q1 **Photosynthesis** is the process that produces 'food' in plants.
Use some of the words below to complete the equation for photosynthesis.

oxygen   carbon dioxide   nitrogen   water   glucose   sodium chloride

.... + ... $\xrightarrow[\text{chlorophyll}]{\text{sunlight}}$ .... + ...

Q2 Plants are made up of cells, tissues, organs and organs systems.

a) Name **three** organs found in a plant.

....

b) Describe the purpose of each of the tissues below in a plant.

Mesophyll tissue: ....

Epidermal tissue: ....

Xylem and phloem: ....

Q3 The rate of photosynthesis in some pondweed was recorded by counting
the bubbles produced per minute at equal intervals during the day.

No. bubbles per minute	Time of day
0	06.00
10	12.00
20	18.00
0	

a) The time for the final reading is missing.
Predict what the time is likely to be.

....

b) Explain why the rate of photosynthesis is 0 bubbles per minute for this time of day.

....

c) Suggest where plants get their food from at this time of day.

....

d) Plot a bar graph on the grid on the right to
display the results shown on the table.

Don't forget about the scales on your graph.

No. bubbles per minute

Time of day

Biology 2a — Cells, Organs and Populations

Plant Structure and Photosynthesis

Q4 The graph below shows the **oxygen** and **carbon dioxide** exchanged by a plant.
The concentration of each gas was measured next to the leaves as light intensity increased.

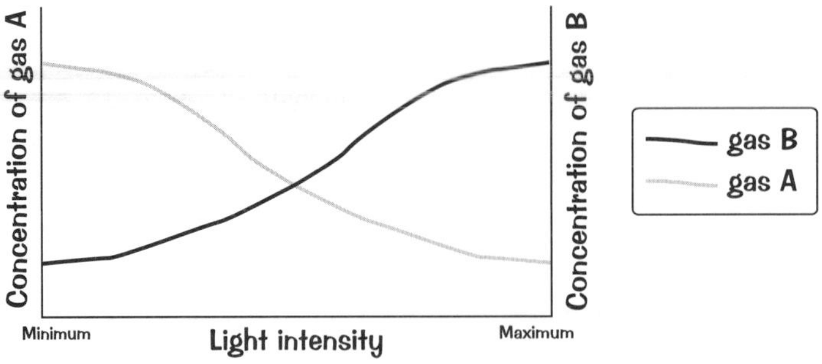

gas B
gas A

a) **i)** Which gas is oxygen and which is carbon dioxide?

Gas A is ....   Gas B is ....

ii) Explain how you decided.

....

....

b) State the relationships between the following:

i) the light intensity and the concentration of carbon dioxide.

....

ii) the light intensity and the concentration of oxygen.

....

Q5 Jack conducted an experiment to investigate the effect of light on photosynthesis. He placed one plant (plant A) in the **dark** for 24 hours, and another plant (plant B) in bright **sunlight**. Jack tested a leaf from each plant for **starch**.

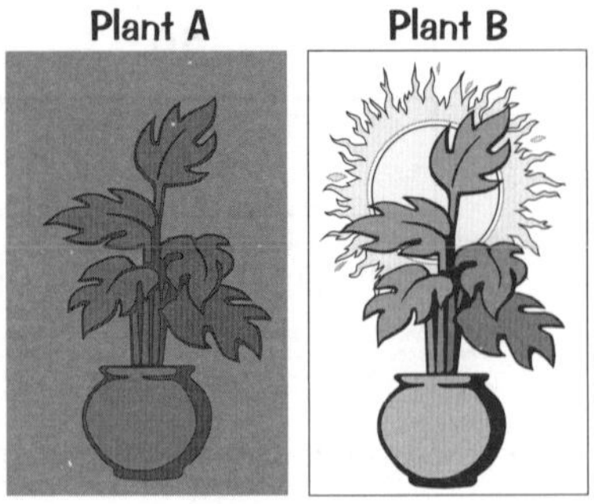

Plant A   Plant B

a) Which plant would you expect to contain more starch?

....

b) Explain your answer to part **a)** above.

....

....

c) Where in the palisade cells of leaves does photosynthesis happen? ....

Top Tips: If you get stuck on a photosynthesis question, jot down the good old equation. You'll see what's needed for photosynthesis and what's produced, which should help you out. Hooray.

The Rate of Photosynthesis

Q1 Below are some straightforward questions about **limiting factors**. Hooray.

a) List **three** factors that can limit the rate of photosynthesis.

....

b) Explain the meaning of the term "limiting factor".

....

c) The limiting factor at a particular time depends on the environmental conditions, e.g. season (such as winter). Name two other environmental conditions that may affect the rate of photosynthesis.

....

Q2 Seth investigated the effect of different concentrations of **carbon dioxide** on the rate of photosynthesis of his Swiss cheese plant. He measured the rate of photosynthesis with increasing light intensity at **three** different CO_2 concentrations. The results are shown on the graph below.

a) What effect does increasing the concentration of CO_2 have on the rate of photosynthesis?

....

....

b) Explain why all the graphs level off eventually.

....

....

Think about the third limiting factor.

Q3 Sunlight contains light of different **wavelengths**, some of which we see as different **colours**. The amount of light absorbed at each wavelength for the green pigment **chlorophyll** is shown below.

a) What wavelengths and colours of light are best absorbed by chlorophyll?

....

b) Suggest how you could use the information on the graph to increase the growth rate of plants in a greenhouse.

....

Q4 Explain why a farmer should ideally have **enough** CO_2 in his greenhouse but **not too much**.

....

....

The Rate of Photosynthesis

Q5 Lucy investigated the **volume of oxygen** produced by pondweed at **different intensities of light**. Her results are shown in the table below.

Relative light intensity	1	2	3	4	5
Volume of oxygen evolved in 10 minutes (ml)	12	25	13	48	61

bubbles of oxygen

pondweed

a) What was Lucy measuring by recording the volume of oxygen produced?

....

b) Plot a graph of her results.

c) i) One of Lucy's results is probably wrong. Circle this point on the graph.

ii) Suggest what error Lucy might have made when she collected this result.

....

....

....

d) Describe the relationship shown on the graph between light intensity and photosynthesis rate.

....

....

e) Would you expect this relationship to continue if Lucy continued to increase the light intensity? Explain your answer.

....

....

Q6 Farmer Fred doesn't put his cows out during the winter because the grass is not growing.

a) State **two** differences between summer and winter conditions that affect the rate of photosynthesis in the grass.

1. ....

2. ....

b) How are the rate of photosynthesis and the growth rate of grass related?

....

....

The Rate of Photosynthesis

Q7   Graham decided to build a **greenhouse** to grow his plants in.

a)   List **three** reasons why a greenhouse is an ideal environment for growing plants.

....

....

....

b)   i)   What could Graham add to his greenhouse in the **winter** for better growth?

....

ii)   What should he add in the **summer** to ensure it doesn't get too hot?

....

iii) What addition would be useful at **night** if he wants the plants to continue photosynthesising?

....

iv) Why might it be better to install a **paraffin heater** rather than an electric heater?

....

Q8   Average daytime summer temperatures in different habitats around the world are recorded in the table below.

Habitat	Temperature (°C)
Forest	19
Arctic	0
Desert	32
Grassland	22
Rainforest	27

a)   Plot a **bar chart** for these results on the grid.

b)   From the values for temperature, in which area would you expect fewest plants to grow?

....

c)   Suggest a reason for your answer above using the terms **enzymes** and **photosynthesis**.

....

....

d)   **Explain** why very few plants can usually grow in the desert even though it has a much higher average temperature than the rainforest where many varieties of plants can grow.

....

12

How Plants Use Glucose

Q1   Complete the passage below by choosing the most appropriate words from the list below.

convert	leaves	margarine	cells	cellulose
cooking oil		energy	walls	lipids

Plants make glucose in their .... Some of it is used for respiration,

which releases .... and allows the plant to ....

the rest of the glucose into other substances and build new ....

In rapidly growing plants, glucose is converted into .... to build cell

.... Seeds can store glucose in the form of ....

For example, we use seeds to make .... and ....

Q2   Plants use glucose to make **protein**. Humans eat plants and animals as sources of protein.

a)   What ions do plants need to absorb from the soil in order to produce protein? ....

b)   Below is a graph comparing the nutrients in dhal and steak, including their protein content.
What percentage of your recommended daily allowance
of protein is provided by 100 g of the following?

Comparison of nutrients in dhal and steak

dhal ....

Dhal is just lentils.

steak ....

c)   Which of these two foods provides a better source of
dietary nutrients in general? Explain your choice.

....

....

d)   Suggest where the amino acids that make up the protein found in steak originally came from.

....

Q3   New potato plants are grown from potato **tubers**, which are stores of **starch**.

a)   Suggest how the new plants obtain the energy needed for growth.

....

b)   Explain why the plants no longer need this energy source once they have grown above the soil.

....

c)   Why do the tubers store starch, not glucose?

....

Distribution of Organisms

Q1 Tick the boxes to show whether the following statements are **true** or **false**.

True False

a) A habitat is the place where an organism lives. ☐ ☐

b) The distribution of an organism is how an organism interacts with its habitat. ☐ ☐

c) You can use quadrats to study the distribution of an organism. ☐ ☐

Q2 Name **three** environmental factors that may affect where an organism is found.

1. ....

2. ....

3. ....

Q3 Dan wanted to investigate the number of **daisies** on his school field. He placed a 1 m² quadrat down at **eight random points** in the field and counted the number of daisies in each quadrat. He recorded his results in the table shown below.

Quadrat number	1	2	3	4	5	6	7	8
Number of daisies	3	1	2	1	4	3	0	2

a) What is a quadrat?

....

b) Suggest one way that Dan could make sure his quadrats are placed at random points.

....

....

c) i) Calculate the mean number of daisies per quadrat in the field.

....

ii) What is the median number of daisies per quadrat?

....

d) The total area of the field is 5 600 m².
Use your answer to **c) i)** to estimate the number of daisies in the whole of the field.

....

Top Tips: Some questions may feel like you're doing maths rather than biology... but you can't get away from things like averages — you do need to know how to work them out for the exam. Booo.

More on the Distribution of Organisms

Q1 Sandy uses a **transect** to investigate buttercup distribution from the middle of a field to a pond.

   a) **i)** On the diagram below, draw **one** way that Sandy could set up her transect.

MIDDLE OF FIELD

POND

     ii) Describe how Sandy could use the transect you've drawn above in her investigation.

....

....

   b) Give **one** way in which Sandy could make her results more reliable.

....

   c) The results of Sandy's investigation are shown in the table below.

Distance away from pond (m)	2	4	6	8	10
Number of buttercups per m²	26	19	14	9	5

     i) Describe the **correlation** between the number of buttercups and the distance from the pond.

....

     ii) Suggest a reason for the correlation.

....

....

Q2 Bill carried out a similar investigation to Sandy's in a field next to a wood. Between the edge of the wood and the field is a small stream. Bill found the number of **dandelions** decreased from the middle of the field to the wood. He wanted to see if the difference in distribution of dandelions was due to a difference in **light intensity**, so he measured light intensity and found it also decreased towards the wood.

Explain why Bill's data isn't valid.

....

....

....

Mixed Questions — Biology 2a

Q1 Draw lines to match up the words below with their correct definition.

Tissue

Diffusion

Habitat

Mode

Photosynthesis

Limiting factor

Differentiation

The place where an organism lives.

The process that produces 'food' (glucose) in plants and algae.

Something that stops photosynthesis from happening any faster.

A group of similar cells that work together to carry out a certain function.

The process by which cells become specialised for a particular job.

The most common value in a set of data.

The spreading out of particles from an area of high concentration to an area of low concentration.

Q2 Cells in **plants** are different from cells in animals.

a) Name **three** parts that are found in plant cells but **not** in animal cells.

1. .... 2. .... 3. ....

b) Palisade cells are a type of plant cell.

i) Complete this diagram of a palisade cell by filling in the labels.

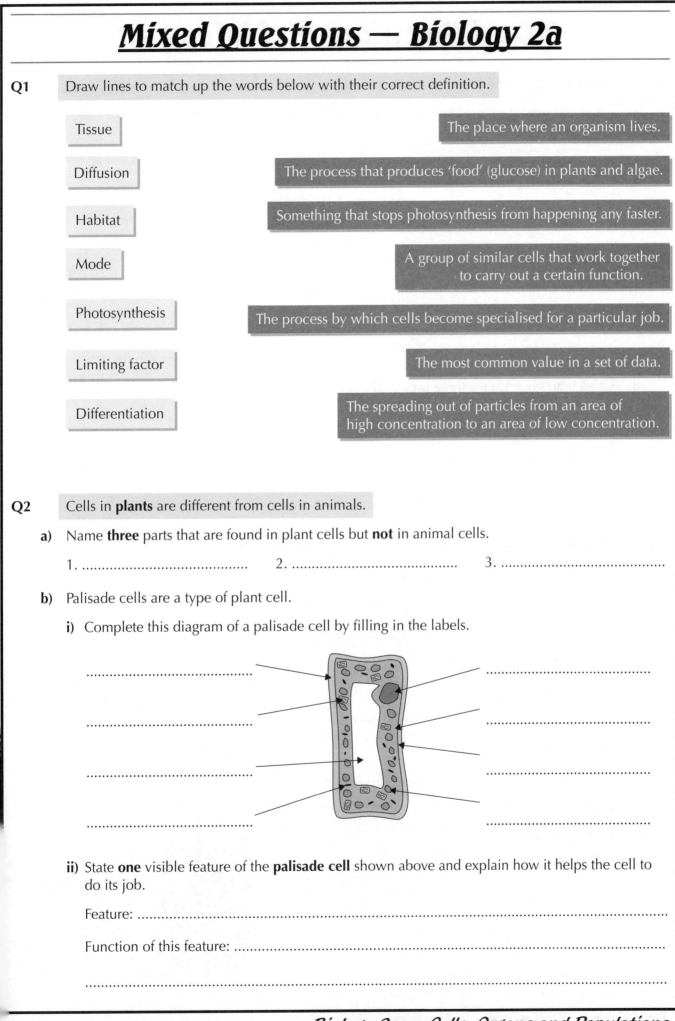

....

....

....

....

....

....

....

....

ii) State **one** visible feature of the **palisade cell** shown above and explain how it helps the cell to do its job.

Feature: ....

Function of this feature: ....

....

Mixed Questions — Biology 2a

Q3   Plants use photosynthesis to produce glucose.

a)   Name the substance in a plant that absorbs light energy during photosynthesis.

....

b)   Circle **two** raw materials needed for photosynthesis from the options given below.

carbon dioxide   oxygen   food   water   nitrogen   helium

c)   Plants store some of the glucose for use when photosynthesis isn't happening.

i)   What do plants store glucose as? ....

ii)   Name **one** place in a plant where the glucose is stored.

....

d)   Other than storage, give **three uses** of glucose for plants.

1. ....

2. ....

3. ....

Q4   **Animals** are made up of cells, tissues, organs and organ systems.

a)   Name the part(s) of a typical animal cell:

i)   where energy is released from glucose, ...

ii)   where most of the chemical reactions happen.   ....

b)   What does muscular tissue do?

....

c)   Describe the **function** of the following organs:

i)   the small intestine   ....

ii)   the large intestine   ....

d)   Label the following organs on the picture of part of the digestive system:

i)   the pancreas

ii)   the liver

Mixed Questions — Biology 2a

Q5   A student was given **three solutions** labelled X, Y and Z. He set up the experiment shown below and left it for a day. At the end of the experiment, the water outside the membrane contained particles X and Y, but not Z.

solutions X, Y and Z

water

a)   Name the process by which particles of X and Y moved through the membrane.

....

b)   What can you conclude about the relative sizes of the X, Y and Z particles?

....

c)   Solutions X, Y and Z were in fact amino acid, protein and glucose solutions. Which of these solutions was substance Z? Explain your answer.

....

....

Q6   Some students wanted to estimate the size of the population of **clover plants** around their school.

a)   What piece of equipment should they use?

....

b)   The school field is 250 m long by 180 m wide. Hannah counted 11 clover plants in a 1 m² area of the field. Approximately how many clover plants are there likely to be on the whole field?

....

c)   Lisa decided to collect data from five different 1 m² areas of the school field. Her results are shown in the table below.

	Area 1	Area 2	Area 3	Area 4	Area 5
No. of plants	11	9	8	9	7

   i) Calculate the **mean** number of clover plants per m² in Lisa's survey.

   ....

   ii) Use Lisa's data to estimate the population size of clover plants on the field.

   ....

d)   Whose estimation of population size is likely to be more accurate? Explain your answer.

....

Biology 2b — Enzymes and Genetics

Enzymes

Q1 a) Write a definition of the word '**enzyme**'.

....

b) In the space below draw a sketch to show how an enzyme's **shape** allows it to break substances down.

Q2 Complete the passage about **proteins** using some of the words given below.

increases	catalyst	high	fats	hormones
amino acids	decreases	proteins	structural	body	sugars

A .... is a substance which .... the speed of a

reaction without being changed or used up. Enzymes catalyse the useful reactions going

on inside cells. All enzymes are .... , which are molecules made

up of long chains of .... These chains fold up into the specific

shapes that enzymes need to do their jobs. Proteins also act as ....

components of tissues, ... and antibodies.

Q3 This graph shows the results from an investigation into the effect of **temperature** on the rate of an **enzyme** catalysed reaction.

Rate of reaction

0 °C   45 °C   Temp.

a) What is the **optimum** temperature for this enzyme?

....

b) What happens to enzymes at temperatures **above** their optimum?

....

Enzymes

Q4 Stuart has a sample of an enzyme and he is trying to find out what its **optimum pH** is. Stuart tests the enzyme by **timing** how long it takes to break down a substance at different pH levels. The results of Stuart's experiment are shown below.

pH	time taken for reaction in seconds
2	101
4	83
6	17
8	76
10	99
12	102

a) Draw a line graph of the results on the grid below.

b) Roughly what is the **optimum** pH for the enzyme?

....

c) Explain why the reaction is very slow at certain pH levels.

....

....

d) Would you expect to find this enzyme in the stomach? Explain your answer.

....

e) Describe two things that Stuart would need to do to make sure his experiment is a fair test.

1. ....

2. ....

Top Tips: Enzymes crop up a lot in Biology so it's worth spending plenty of time making sure you know all the basics. If you're finding things a bit dull, you could always take a little break and eat some tofu to make sure you have enough protein to make lots of delightful enzymes.

Enzymes and Digestion

Q1 Fill in the boxes to show how the **three main food groups** are **broken down** during digestion.

a)

[_____]

↓

protein ⟶ [_____]

b)

lipase

↓

[_____] ⟶ [_____] + [_____]

c)

[_____]

↓

carbohydrate ⟶ [_____]
e.g. starch

Q2 Choose from the words below to complete the table showing where **amylase**, **protease**, **lipase** and **bile** are made. You may use some words more than once and you might not need some of them.

pancreas   liver   salivary glands   small intestine

large intestine   stomach   gall bladder   kidneys

Amylase	Protease	Lipase	Bile

Q3 a) Circle the correct words from each pair to complete this passage about **bile**.

> Bile is stored in the **gall bladder** / **pancreas** before being released into the **liver** / **small intestine**.
>
> Bile **acidifies** / **neutralises** the material from the stomach which provides the optimum pH
>
> for the **enzymes** / **microorganisms** in the rest of the digestive system to work. Bile breaks
>
> **fat** / **glycerol** into smaller droplets.

b) Explain how emulsification helps digestion.

....

....

Finest emulsion

More on Enzymes and Digestion

Q1   Fill in the boxes to label this diagram of the human **digestive system**.

Q2   Tick the correct boxes to show whether the following sentences about **digestion** are **true** or **false**.

True False

a) **Hydrochloric acid** is produced by the liver.

b) Some digestive enzymes are made by special cells in **glands** and then released into the gut.

c) Specialised cells in the **lining of the gut** can also produce digestive enzymes.

d) **Pepsin** works best in alkaline conditions.

Q3   Describe the role of each of the following in **digestion**:

a) Salivary glands

   ....

b) Pancreas

   ....

c) Liver

   ....

Top Tips: This stuff is pretty easy so it shouldn't take you long to learn. The trickiest bits are probably the roles of the liver and pancreas — make sure you've got those clear in your head.

Enzymes and Respiration

Q1 **a)** Circle the correct word equation for **aerobic respiration**.

glucose + oxygen → carbon dioxide + water (+ energy)

protein + oxygen → carbon dioxide + water (+ energy)

glucose + carbon dioxide → oxygen + water (+ energy)

b) What does the term 'aerobic respiration' mean?

....

Q2 **a)** Tick the correct boxes to show whether the sentences are true or false.

True   False

i) Aerobic respiration releases energy.   ☐ ☐

ii) Respiration usually releases energy from protein.   ☐ ☐

iii) Aerobic respiration is more efficient than anaerobic respiration.   ☐ ☐

iv) Respiration takes place in a cell's nucleus.   ☐ ☐

v) Aerobic respiration produces carbon dioxide.   ☐ ☐

vi) Breathing is a kind of respiration.   ☐ ☐

vii) Respiration goes on all the time in both plants and animals.   ☐ ☐

viii) Respiration involves reactions catalysed by enzymes.   ☐ ☐

b) Write a correct version of each false sentence in the space below.

....

....

....

Q3 Give **four** examples of things that animals and / or plants use **energy** for.

1. ....

2. ....

3. ....

4. ....

Top Tips: Hmm, respiration, there isn't really much to say other than make sure you learn the word equation and remember that IT'S NOT THE SAME AS BREATHING.

Exercise

Q1 Complete the following sentences by circling the correct words from each pair.

a) During exercise our muscles need more **energy** / **water** to enable them to keep **relaxing** / **contracting**.

b) This means they need a continuous supply of **protein** / **glucose** and **carbon dioxide** / **oxygen**.

c) During vigorous exercise muscles use glucose **slowly** / **rapidly**, so some of the stored **glycogen** / **oxygen** is converted back to glucose to provide more energy.

d) If your body can't supply enough oxygen to the muscles during exercise they start doing **aerobic** / **anaerobic** respiration.

e) Anaerobic respiration is the **complete** / **incomplete** breakdown of glucose.

Q2 John has to **sprint** for the bus because he is late.

a) State **two** effects this sudden physical exercise has on John's body.

1. ....

2. ....

b) After his initial sprint, John's leg muscles become tired and stop contracting efficiently.

i) What name is given to this effect? ....

ii) Suggest the substance that is causing this effect. ....

iii) What **process** produces this substance? ....

c) When he gets on the bus he's out of breath.
Explain why he continues to breathe deeply for a while.

....

....

....

Q3 a) Use some of the words given below to complete the word equation for **anaerobic respiration**.

carbon dioxide   oxygen   lactic acid   water   glucose   energy

Anaerobic: .... → .... (+ ....)

b) Does anaerobic respiration produce **more** or **less** energy than aerobic respiration?

....

Exercise

Q4 Jim is a keen runner. He takes part in a 400 metre race. The **graph** below shows Jim's **breathing rate** before, during and after the race.

a) How much does Jim's breathing rate go up during the race? .... **breaths per minute**

b) Explain why exercise makes Jim's breathing rate increase.

....

....

....

c) How long does it take for Jim's breathing rate return to normal after the race?

....

Q5 Roy wants to find out which of his friends has the shortest **'recovery' time**. Your recovery time is how long it takes for your pulse rate to **return to normal** after exercise. Roy tests his friends separately. He measures their **pulse rate**, then asks them to **run** for 2 minutes. After they've finished running, he measures their pulse rate at 15 second intervals until it has returned to normal.

a) Write down **two** things Roy should do to ensure it is a **fair test**.

Think about keeping things constant.

1. ....

....

2. ....

b) Here is a sketch of Roy's results.
Which of his friends had the **shortest**
recovery time?

KEY
— Jim
— Saeed
— Bonnie

....

Biology 2b — Enzymes and Genetics

Uses of Enzymes

Q1 **Enzymes** are often used in industrial processes to alter foods.
Explain how enzymes can be used in making:

a) baby foods.

....

....

b) 'slimming' foods.

....

....

....

Q2 The picture below shows two types of **washing powder**.

Lipaclean
Contains lipase enzymes

Protewash
packed with proteases

a) Which of the two washing powders would you recommend to someone who has dripped
butter on their shirt? Explain your answer.

....

....

b) Why are some people unable to use washing powders like these?

....

Q3 Complete the following sentences by circling the correct words from each pair.

a) Starch and sugar are both **proteins / carbohydrates / fats**.

b) Starch syrup **is / isn't** sweet. Sugar syrup **is / isn't** sweet.

c) You can convert starch syrup into sugar syrup by adding **lipases / carbohydrases / proteases**.

Uses of Enzymes

Q4   **Enzymes** are often used in **industrial processes**.

a)   Why are enzymes used in industrial processes?

....

b)   Name **two** conditions that need to be carefully controlled for the enzymes to work efficiently.

1. ....

2. ....

c)   i)   Give **two advantages** of using enzymes in industry.

1. ....

....

2. ....

....

ii) Give **one disadvantage** of using enzymes in industry.

....

....

Q5   Caroline is testing the effectiveness of two different **washing powders** at getting out food stains. She washes stained clothes in both powders, at different temperatures. Then she records their **effectiveness** using a scale of **1** (**poor**) to **10** (**excellent**).

a)   Name **one** thing that Caroline must do to make sure that her experiment is a fair test.

....

b)   Caroline's results are shown in the table on the right.

i)   State which powder is best at cleaning food stains at 30 °C.

....

ii) Which of the powders is a **biological detergent**? Explain your answer.

....

....

	Washing powder	
Effectiveness	A	B
Temperature: 20 °C	5	2
Temperature: 30 °C	8	4
Temperature: 40 °C	9	6

Top Tips: Each enzyme catalyses a specific reaction, e.g. proteases break down proteins. This means enzymes can be really useful, e.g. proteases are put in biological detergents. However, when using them, you have to keep conditions tightly controlled otherwise they will be denatured.

Biology 2b — Enzymes and Genetics

DNA

Q1 DNA contains all the **instructions** to make a living organism.

a) What does DNA stand for? ....

b) Fill in the blanks in the paragraph below using words from the list.

| cells | chromosomes | cytoplasm | gene | amino acids | section | protein | fat |

DNA is found in the nucleus of animal and plant .... in very long molecules

called .... A gene is a .... of DNA. Each gene contains

instructions for the cell to make a specific .... Cells make proteins by

connecting .... together in a particular order.

c) How many amino acids are used to make proteins in the human body? ....

d) DNA molecules have a special twisted structure. Give the name of this structure.

....

e) Is everyone's DNA unique? Explain your answer.

....

Q2 **Genetic fingerprinting** is a way of comparing people's DNA — it's useful in forensic science. Put these following stages of DNA fingerprinting into the correct order.

Compare the unique patterns of DNA.

Collect the sample for DNA testing.

Separate the sections of DNA.

Cut the DNA into small sections.

1. ....

2. ....

3. ....

4. ....

Q3 A national **genetic database** would allow everyone's unique pattern of DNA to be saved on file.

a) Give one use of a national genetic database.

....

b) Give one drawback of a national genetic database.

....

DNA

Q4 A thoroughbred horse breeder has collected DNA samples from each of her horses. Her **new foal's DNA** is **sample 1**. The **mother** of the foal provided **sample 2**. Study the **DNA profiles** and complete the table showing which horse is the **foal's father**.

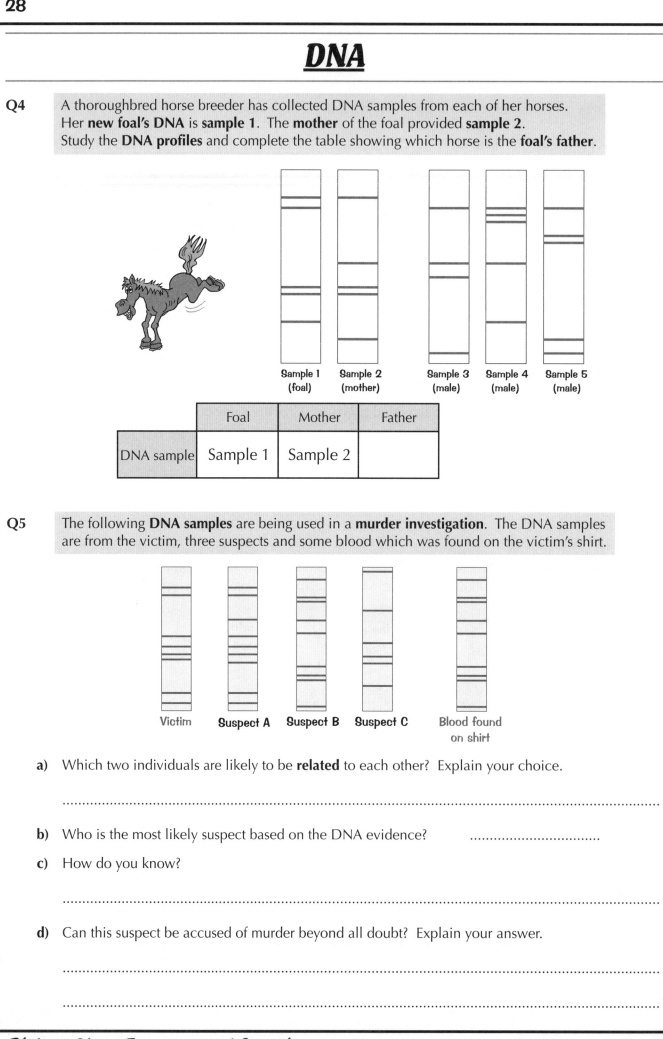

Sample 1 (foal) Sample 2 (mother) Sample 3 (male) Sample 4 (male) Sample 5 (male)

	Foal	Mother	Father
DNA sample	Sample 1	Sample 2	

Q5 The following **DNA samples** are being used in a **murder investigation**. The DNA samples are from the victim, three suspects and some blood which was found on the victim's shirt.

Victim Suspect A Suspect B Suspect C Blood found on shirt

a) Which two individuals are likely to be **related** to each other? Explain your choice.

....

b) Who is the most likely suspect based on the DNA evidence? ....

c) How do you know?

....

d) Can this suspect be accused of murder beyond all doubt? Explain your answer.

....

....

Biology 2b — Enzymes and Genetics

Cell Division — Mitosis

Q1 Decide whether the following statements are **true** or **false**.

	True	False
a) There are 46 chromosomes in most of your body cells.	☐	☐
b) There are 20 pairs of chromosomes in a human cheek cell.	☐	☐
c) Chromosomes are found in the cytoplasm of a cell.	☐	☐
d) Before a cell divides by mitosis, it duplicates its DNA.	☐	☐
e) Mitosis is where a cell splits to create two genetically identical copies.	☐	☐
f) Mitosis produces new cells to replace those which are damaged.	☐	☐
g) We need mitosis to grow.	☐	☐

Q2 The following diagrams show the different stages of **mitosis**.
Draw lines to match the description of each stage with the correct diagram.

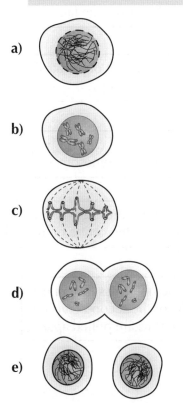

a)

b)

c)

d)

e)

A membrane forms in each half of the cell to form the nuclei.

Cells that are not dividing contain long strings of DNA.

The cytoplasm divides, making two new genetically identical cells.

The chromosomes line up across the centre of the cell, and then the arms of each chromosome are pulled to opposite ends of the cell.

Before a cell divides, it copies (duplicates) its DNA and forms X-shaped chromosomes.

Q3 Complete the following passage using the words below.

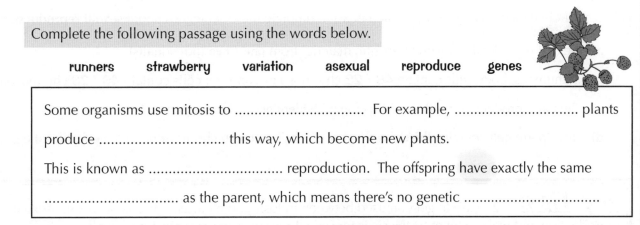

runners   strawberry   variation   asexual   reproduce   genes

Some organisms use mitosis to .... For example, ... plants

produce .... this way, which become new plants.

This is known as .... reproduction. The offspring have exactly the same

.... as the parent, which means there's no genetic ....

Cell Division — Meiosis

Q1   Tick the boxes below to show which statements are true of **meiosis**.

		True	False
a)	Halves the number of chromosomes.	☐	☐
b)	Chromosomes line up in the centre of the cell.	☐	☐
c)	Forms cells that are genetically different.	☐	☐
d)	In humans, it only happens in the reproductive organs.	☐	☐
e)	Doesn't form gametes.	☐	☐

Q2   Draw lines to match the descriptions of the stages of **meiosis** to the right diagrams below.

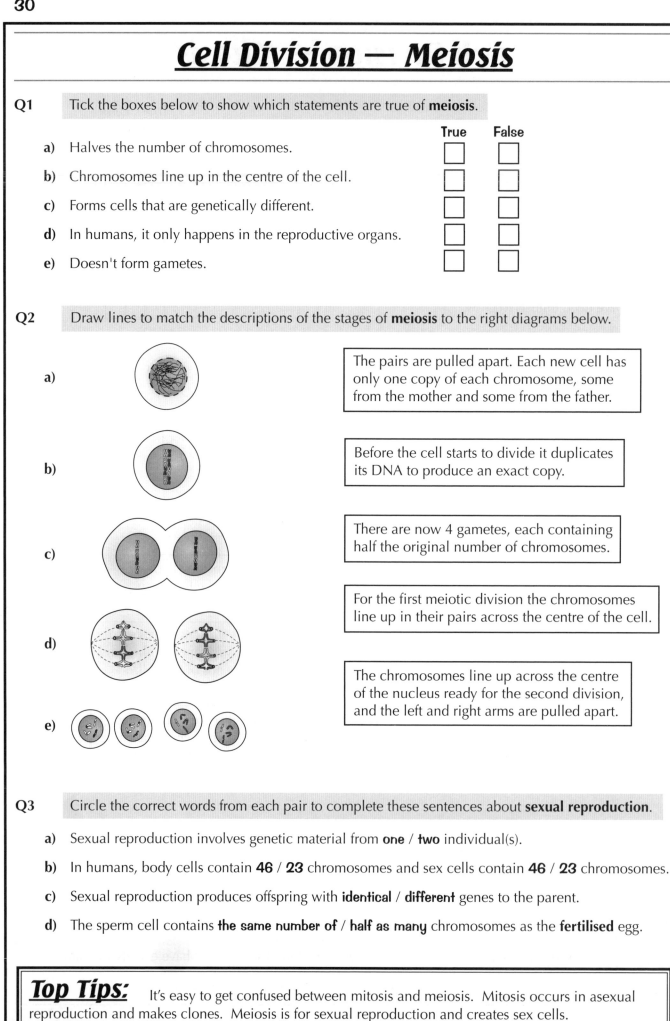

a)

The pairs are pulled apart. Each new cell has only one copy of each chromosome, some from the mother and some from the father.

b)

Before the cell starts to divide it duplicates its DNA to produce an exact copy.

c)

There are now 4 gametes, each containing half the original number of chromosomes.

d)

For the first meiotic division the chromosomes line up in their pairs across the centre of the cell.

e)

The chromosomes line up across the centre of the nucleus ready for the second division, and the left and right arms are pulled apart.

Q3   Circle the correct words from each pair to complete these sentences about **sexual reproduction**.

a)   Sexual reproduction involves genetic material from **one** / **two** individual(s).

b)   In humans, body cells contain **46** / **23** chromosomes and sex cells contain **46** / **23** chromosomes.

c)   Sexual reproduction produces offspring with **identical** / **different** genes to the parent.

d)   The sperm cell contains **the same number of** / **half as many** chromosomes as the **fertilised** egg.

Top Tips: It's easy to get confused between mitosis and meiosis. Mitosis occurs in asexual reproduction and makes clones. Meiosis is for sexual reproduction and creates sex cells.

Cell Division — Meiosis

Q4   Mosquitoes have **three pairs** of **chromosomes** in their body cells.
The diagram below shows a mosquito cell that is about to divide by **meiosis**.

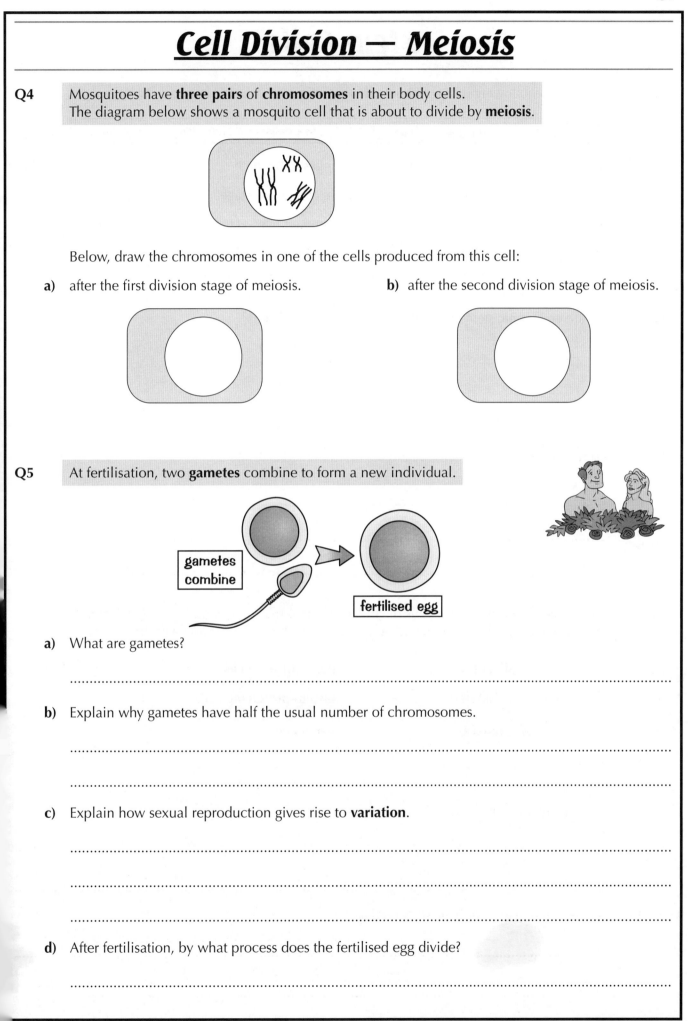

Below, draw the chromosomes in one of the cells produced from this cell:

a) after the first division stage of meiosis.

b) after the second division stage of meiosis.

Q5   At fertilisation, two **gametes** combine to form a new individual.

gametes combine

fertilised egg

a) What are gametes?

....

b) Explain why gametes have half the usual number of chromosomes.

....

....

c) Explain how sexual reproduction gives rise to **variation**.

....

....

....

d) After fertilisation, by what process does the fertilised egg divide?

....

Stem Cells

Q1   Complete the following passage about **differentiation** using words from the list below.

| plant | embryos | specialised | sex cells | stem cells | animal |

Differentiation is the way in which a cell changes to become .... for its job.

.... cells usually differentiate at an early stage. Most ....

cells keep the ability to differentiate throughout their lives. Undifferentiated cells that can

develop into many different types of cell are called ....

Q2   How are **embryonic** stem cells different from **adult** stem cells?

....

....

Q3   Describe a way that stem cells are already used in medicine.

....

....

....

Q4   In the future, **embryonic stem cells** might be used to replace faulty cells in sick people.
Match the problems below to the potential cures which could be made with stem cells.

diabetes	**heart muscle cells**
paralysis	**insulin-producing cells**
heart disease	**nerve cells**

Q5   People have **different opinions** when it comes to **stem cell research**.

a)   Give one argument **in favour** of stem cell research.

....

....

b)   Give one argument **against** stem cell research.

....

....

X and Y Chromosomes

Q1   Tick the boxes to show whether each statement is **true** or **false**.

                                                                      True   **False**

   a)   Women have two X chromosomes. Men have an X and a Y chromosome.

   b)   There is a 75% chance that a couple's first child will be a girl.

   c)   Sperm cells (male gametes) can carry an X or a Y chromosome.

   d)   If you have 4 children, you will always get 2 boys and 2 girls.

Q2   Here is a genetic diagram showing the inheritance of **sex chromosomes** in humans.

   a)   Complete the diagram to show the combinations of chromosomes in the offspring.

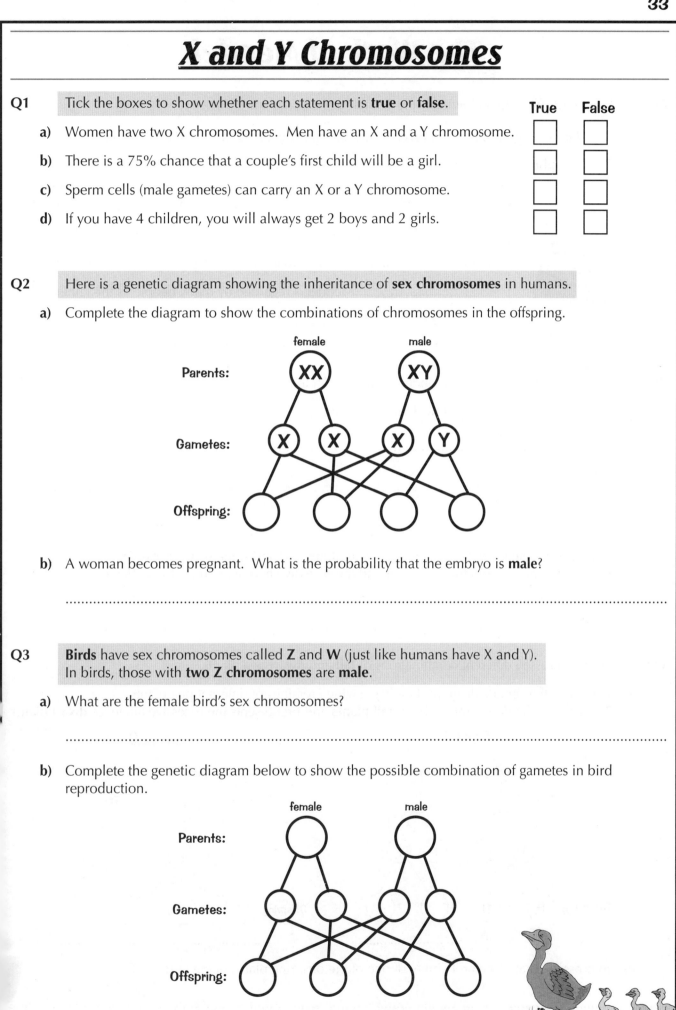

   b)   A woman becomes pregnant. What is the probability that the embryo is **male**?

   ....

Q3   **Birds** have sex chromosomes called **Z** and **W** (just like humans have X and Y).
       In birds, those with **two Z chromosomes** are **male**.

   a)   What are the female bird's sex chromosomes?

   ....

   b)   Complete the genetic diagram below to show the possible combination of gametes in bird
        reproduction.

The Work of Mendel

Q1   Use words from the following list to complete the paragraph below.

> leaf   genetics   monk   double-glazing salesman   1866   viruses
>
> physicist   characteristics   1980   generation   bulbs

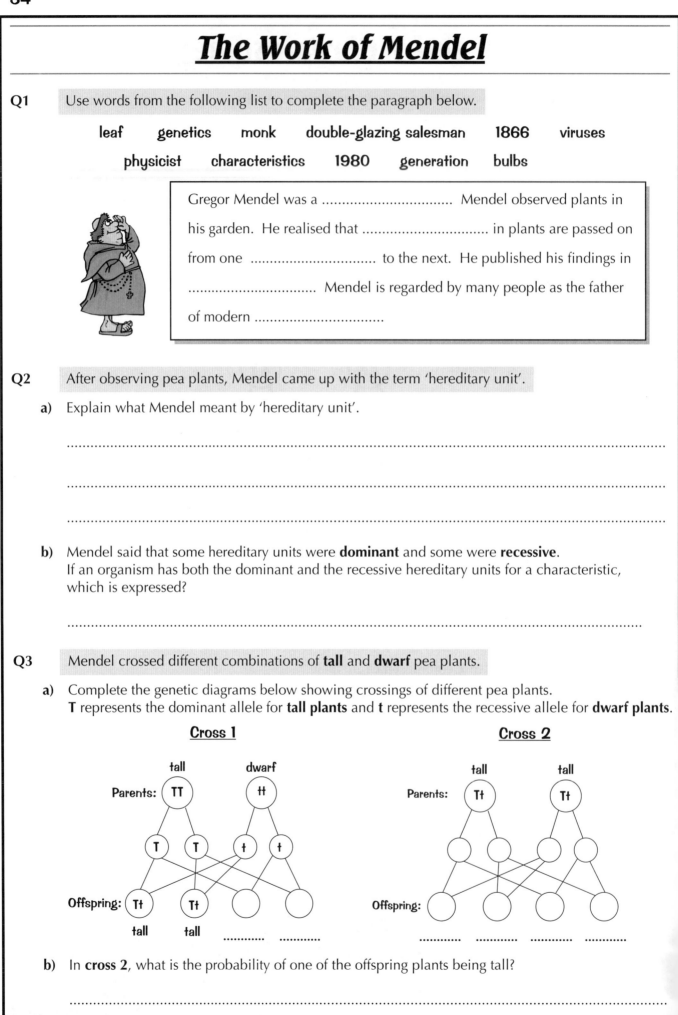

Gregor Mendel was a .... Mendel observed plants in his garden. He realised that .... in plants are passed on from one .... to the next. He published his findings in .... Mendel is regarded by many people as the father of modern ....

Q2   After observing pea plants, Mendel came up with the term 'hereditary unit'.

a)   Explain what Mendel meant by 'hereditary unit'.

....

....

....

b)   Mendel said that some hereditary units were **dominant** and some were **recessive**.
If an organism has both the dominant and the recessive hereditary units for a characteristic, which is expressed?

....

Q3   Mendel crossed different combinations of **tall** and **dwarf** pea plants.

a)   Complete the genetic diagrams below showing crossings of different pea plants.
T represents the dominant allele for **tall plants** and **t** represents the recessive allele for **dwarf plants**.

Cross 1   **Cross 2**

Parents: TT (tall)   tt (dwarf)   Parents: Tt (tall)   Tt (tall)

Offspring: Tt (tall)   Tt (tall)   ....   Offspring: ....

b)   In **cross 2**, what is the probability of one of the offspring plants being tall?

....

Genetic Diagrams

Q1   Draw lines to match each of the terms below with its meaning.

dominant	having two different alleles for a gene
genotype	having two identical alleles for a gene
heterozygous	shown in organisms heterozygous for that trait
homozygous	not shown in organisms heterozygous for that trait
phenotype	the actual characteristics of an individual
recessive	the alleles that an individual contains

Q2   Wilma carries a **recessive** allele for **red** hair and a **dominant** allele for **brown** hair.

a)   What is Wilma's natural hair colour?

....

b)   Is Wilma homozygous or heterozygous for this characteristic?

....

Q3   Fruit flies usually have **red** eyes. However, there are a small number of white-eyed fruit flies. Having **white** eyes is a **recessive** characteristic.

a)   Complete the following sentences with either '**red eyes**' or '**white eyes**'.

i) **R** is the allele for ....

ii) **r** is the allele for ....

iii) Fruit flies with alleles **RR** or **Rr** will have ....

iv) Fruit flies with the alleles **rr** will have ....

b)   Two fruit flies have the alleles **Rr**. They fall in love and get it on.

i)   Complete this genetic diagram to show the possible offspring. One's been done for you.

parent's alleles

		R	r
parent's alleles	**R**	RR	
	r		

Read down and across to work out what combination of alleles should be in each box.

ii) What is the probability that the fruit flies' offspring will have **white eyes**?

....

iii) The fruit flies have 16 offspring. How many of the offspring are **likely** to have **red eyes**?

....

Genetic Diagrams

Q4   Seeds of pea plants can be **smooth** or **wrinkled**. The allele for smooth seeds (**S**) is dominant. The allele for wrinkled seeds (**s**) is recessive.

a)   The diagrams below shows a cross between a thoroughbred pea plant with smooth seeds (genetic type **SS**) and a thoroughbred pea plant with wrinkled seeds (genetic type **ss**).

Complete the genetic diagram.

Parents' alleles: SS   ss

Gametes' alleles:

Possible combinations
of alleles in offspring:

b)   In this cross, what is the probability of one offspring producing wrinkled seeds? Tick the correct option.

☐   100% chance of producing wrinkled seeds

☐   50% chance of producing wrinkled seeds

☐   25% chance of producing wrinkled seeds

☐   0% chance of producing wrinkled seeds

Pictures of peas are very dull.
So here's a picture of a tapir instead.

c)   Two hybrid pea plants (**Ss**) are interbred.
Complete the genetic diagram to show the possible combinations of alleles in the offspring.

	parent's alleles	
	S	s
S		
s		

parent's alleles

d)   Is the following statement **true** or **false**? Tick the correct box.

"Mrs Maguire crosses two pea plants with the alleles Ss. If she gets 12 new seedlings as a result, it's most likely that 3 of the seedlings will produce wrinkled seeds."

True False
☐   ☐

Top Tips: Genetic diagrams look like alphabet spaghetti at first — but they're OK really. They're useful for working out the possible combinations of alleles that offspring can get from their parents — and the probability of each combination.

Genetic Disorders

Q1   **Cystic fibrosis** is a **genetic disorder** which affects cell membranes.
It is caused by a **recessive** allele, which can be passed on from parents to their children.

a)   Complete the following genetic diagram showing the inheritance of cystic fibrosis.
The recessive allele for cystic fibrosis is **f**, and the dominant allele is **F**.

Parents: (Ff)   (Ff)

Gametes:

Offspring:

b) i) In the above genetic diagram, what is the probability of a child having cystic fibrosis?

....

     ii) In the above genetic diagram, what is the probability of a child being a carrier of the cystic fibrosis allele (but not having the disease)?

....

c)   Approximately **1 in every 2500** babies born in the UK will have cystic fibrosis.   About 600 000 babies are born in the UK each year.   How many would you expect to have cystic fibrosis?

....

Q2   John is a carrier of **cystic fibrosis**, a **recessive** genetic disorder. His wife
Helen is **not** a carrier of cystic fibrosis (and does not suffer from the disease).

a)   John and Helen are planning a family.

    i) Complete the genetic diagram
on the right to show what alleles
their child might inherit from them.

        Use the symbols **F** and **f**
to represent the alleles.

Helen's alleles

	....	....
....	....	....
....	....	....

John's alleles

    ii) What is the probability that John and Helen's child will suffer from cystic fibrosis?

....

b)   John's brother Mark suffers from cystic fibrosis. Mark's wife is **not** a carrier or a sufferer.
Could a child of theirs suffer from cystic fibrosis? Explain your answer.

....

....

Genetic Disorders

Q3   **Polydactyly** is a **genetic disorder** which causes a baby to be born with **extra fingers or toes**. Polydactyly is caused by a **dominant** allele.

a)   i)   Complete the genetic diagram below showing the inheritance pattern of polydactyly. The dominant allele for polydactyly is **D**, and the recessive allele is **d**.

Parents: (Dd)   (dd)

Gametes:

Offspring:

ii) In the above genetic diagram, what is the probability that a child will be polydactyl?

....

b)   Will a person with the alleles **Dd** be a **sufferer**, a **carrier** or **neither**? Explain your answer.

....

....

c)   State the probability that of a child of two parents with the alleles **DD** and **dd** will be polydactyl.

....

Q4   During in vitro fertilisation (IVF) a cell can be removed from an embryo and **screened** for **genetic disorders**. If a faulty allele is present, the embryo is destroyed.

a)   Explain why some people think embryo screening is a **bad** thing.

....

....

....

b)   Explain why some people think embryo screening is a **good** thing.

....

....

....

More Genetic Diagrams

Q1 An allele for the colour grey (**G**) in mice is dominant over the allele for the colour white (**g**). A hybrid grey mouse (**Gg**) was bred with a thoroughbred white mouse (**gg**).

a) Complete the genetic diagram below to show the potential combinations of alleles in the offspring of the two mice.

Parents: **Gg**   **gg**

Gametes:

Offspring:

'Hybrid' = an organism which has two different alleles for the same characteristic, e.g. Hh.
Thoroughbred = an organism which has two identical alleles for a characteristic, e.g. HH or hh.

b) What is the likely ratio of colours in any litters of offspring (grey : white)?

....

c) If the mice had 12 babies, how many would there be **likely** to be of each colour?

....

Q2 Sally is investigating the inheritance of **flower colours**. She knows that the allele for the colour **red** is **dominant** over the allele for the colour **white**.

Sally has two of the same plant, one with **red** flowers and one with **white** flowers. Suggest how Sally can find out whether the plant with red flowers is thoroughbred red (**RR**) or hybrid red (**Rr**).

....

....

....

....

Q3 An allele for the long hair (**H**) in cats is dominant over the allele for the short hair (**h**). A homozygous long-haired cat (**HH**) was bred with a homozygous short-haired cat (**hh**).

a) In the space below, draw a genetic diagram to show the potential combinations of alleles in the offspring of the two cats.

b) What is the probability of their offspring having:

i) long hair? ....

ii) short hair? ....

More Genetic Diagrams

Q4 The family tree below shows a family with a history of **cystic fibrosis**. Both Libby and Anne are pregnant. They know the sexes of their babies but not whether they have the disorder.

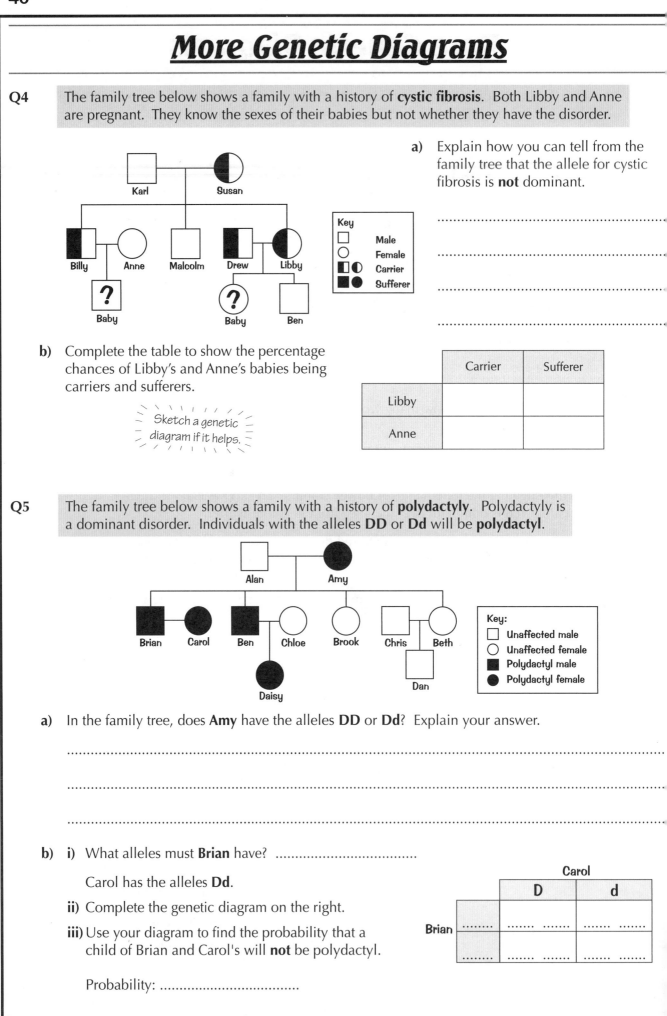

a) Explain how you can tell from the family tree that the allele for cystic fibrosis is **not** dominant.

....

....

....

....

b) Complete the table to show the percentage chances of Libby's and Anne's babies being carriers and sufferers.

Sketch a genetic diagram if it helps.

	Carrier	Sufferer
Libby		
Anne		

Q5 The family tree below shows a family with a history of **polydactyly**. Polydactyly is a dominant disorder. Individuals with the alleles **DD** or **Dd** will be **polydactyl**.

a) In the family tree, does **Amy** have the alleles **DD** or **Dd**? Explain your answer.

....

....

....

b) i) What alleles must **Brian** have? ....

Carol has the alleles **Dd**.

ii) Complete the genetic diagram on the right.

iii) Use your diagram to find the probability that a child of Brian and Carol's will **not** be polydactyl.

Probability: ....

		Carol	
		D	d
Brian	....	....	....
	....	....	....

Fossils

Q1   Scientists can use **fossils** to study what life on Earth used to be like.

a)   What is a fossil?

....

b)   Where are fossils usually found?

....

Q2   Fossils are **formed** in several different ways.

Choose from the words provided to complete the passage about fossil formation.

cast	decays	bones	softens	tissues	shaped
clay	fast	hardens	sediments	slowly	rock

In one type of fossil formation, structures like teeth and .... decay very

.... and are replaced by minerals that form a ....-like

substance .... like the original structure.

In another type of fossil formation, a dead plant or animal is buried in a

...............................-like material which later ....

As the organism decays, a .... is left behind, leaving a clear impression.

Q3   **Fossils** can be formed in places where there is no decay such as in amber or tar pits.

a)   **i)** What is amber?

....

ii) How exactly does amber preserve things?

....

b)   Draw lines to match the reasons for no decay to the types of environment.

No oxygen or moisture   Peat bogs

Too acidic   Glaciers

Too cold   Tar pits

Pete's Bog

Biology 2b — Enzymes and Genetics

Fossils

Q4 It can be hard to find **fossils** of very **early life forms**.

Give **two** reasons why.

1. ....

....

2. ....

....

Q5 Fossils of shells were found in a sample of rock.

a) Explain how a shell lying in sediment at the bottom of the sea could be turned into a fossil.

....

....

....

Think about what replaces the tissues of organisms as they slowly decay.

b) Fossils were found in this sample of rock.
Explain why scientists think fossil B is older than fossil A.

....

....

....

Fossil A

Fossil B

Q6 One idea of **how life began** is that simple organic molecules were brought to Earth by **comets**. It's not known if this is right.

a) What do we call this type of scientific idea? ....

b) Suggest why this idea has neither been generally accepted or completely rejected by all scientists.

....

....

c) Give another scientific idea for how life began.

....

....

___

Top Tips: It's weird to think that looking at squiggles inside rocks (like the one above) can tell you what life used to be like ages ago... Don't forget to learn what fossils are and how they form.

Extinction and Speciation

Q1 Dinosaurs, mammoths and dodos are all animals that are now **extinct**.

a) What does the term 'extinct' mean?

....

....

b) How do we know about extinct animals?

....

....

Q2 There are many reasons why a species might become **extinct**.

Draw lines to match the reasons for extinction on the left with their correct examples on the right.

A catastrophic event kills every member of the species.

The environment changes too quickly.

A new disease kills every member of the species.

Every member of a species of toad is killed when a new fungal pathogen is accidentally introduced to their habitat.

Every member of a species of parrot becomes ill with a flu-like virus but then recovers.

An island's rainforest is completely chopped down, destroying the habitat of the striped monkey.

A rare plant that lives on the side of a volcano is wiped out when the volcano erupts.

Q3 A species is a group of similar organisms that can reproduce to give fertile offspring.

a) Define the term **speciation**.

....

b) How can you tell that speciation has occurred?

....

....

c) "Speciation can lead to extinction."
Tick the correct box to show whether this statement is **true** or **false**.

True False
☐ ☐

Extinction and Speciation

Q4   The diagrams below show the stages of **speciation**.
Draw lines to match the labels to the correct diagrams.

| A new species develops. | The populations adapt to new environments. | There are two populations of the same species. | Physical barriers separate the populations. |

Q5   **Purple banana-eating squirrels** used to found on one specific island but a scientist thinks that they've now become **extinct**. She looks into why this might have happened.

Briefly explain why each of these factors may have led to the squirrel population being wiped out.

a)   A new population of **banana-eating spiders** was introduced to the island.

....

....

b)   Ten **squirrel-eating gibbons** have escaped from the island zoo in the last five years.

....

....

Q6   **Isolation** and **natural selection** can lead to speciation.

a)   What is meant by the term '**isolation**'?

....

b)   The statements below describe how geographical isolation can lead to speciation.
Put them in the **correct order** by numbering the boxes. The first one has been done for you.

☐   The alleles that control the beneficial characteristics are more likely to be passed on to the next generation.

☐   Each population shows variation because they have a wide range of alleles.

☐   Eventually, individuals from the different populations have changed so much that they become separate species.

1   A physical barrier geographically isolates some individuals from the main population.

☐   In each population, individuals with characteristics that make them better adapted to their environment have a better chance of survival and so are more likely to breed successfully.

☐   Conditions on either side of a physical barrier are slightly different.

Mixed Questions — Biology 2b

Q1 **Stem cells** and their uses are a major focus of current medical research.

a) What unique characteristic do stem cells have which ordinary body cells don't have?

....

b) Scientists have experimented with growing stem cells in different conditions.

i) What is the name of the process by which stem cells **divide** for growth?

....

ii) Suggest why scientists are interested in **embryonic** stem cells.

....

....

c) Although there is potential for medical breakthroughs, some people disagree with stem cell research on ethical grounds. Describe one **ethical issue** surrounding stem cell research.

....

....

Q2 In one of Gregor Mendel's experiments, he crossed homozygous purple-flowered pea plants with homozygous white-flowered plants. The **first generation** of offspring were **all purple-flowered**.

a) In Mendel's experiment, which characteristic is recessive?

....

b) Using the symbols **F** and **f** to represent the alleles for **purple** and **white**, write down the combination of alleles (genetic make-up) of each of the following:

i) the original purple-flowered parent plant

....

ii) the original white-flowered parent plant

....

iii) the first generation of purple-flowered offspring

....

c) Mendel crossed **two** of the purple flowers from the **first generation** of offspring. What ratio of purple:white flowers would he expect to get? Explain your answer.

....

....

Mixed Questions — Biology 2b

Q3   **Albinism** is a genetic condition. Affected people, called albinos, lack any skin pigmentation. A couple, neither of whom is albino, have a child who is an albino.

Is the allele for albinism dominant or recessive? Explain your answer.

....

....

....

Q4   Two grey rabbits are mated, and eight offspring are produced. Five of the offspring have grey fur, and three have white fur. The allele for grey fur (**G**) is dominant. The allele for white fur (**g**) is recessive. The **parent rabbits** both have the alleles **Gg**.

a) Draw a **genetic cross diagram** in the space below, to show the **probability** of each combination of alleles occurring in the offspring of the rabbits.

b) **i)** What is the predicted ratio of grey to white rabbits in the offspring?

....

ii) Explain why the actual ratio of colours in the offspring is not exactly the same as this.

....

....

c) If two white rabbits are mated together, what proportion of their offspring will be white? Explain your answer.

....

....

....

Biology 2b — Enzymes and Genetics

Mixed Questions — Biology 2b

Q5 The diagram shows a chalk cliff face and the places where three **fossils** were found in the cliff.

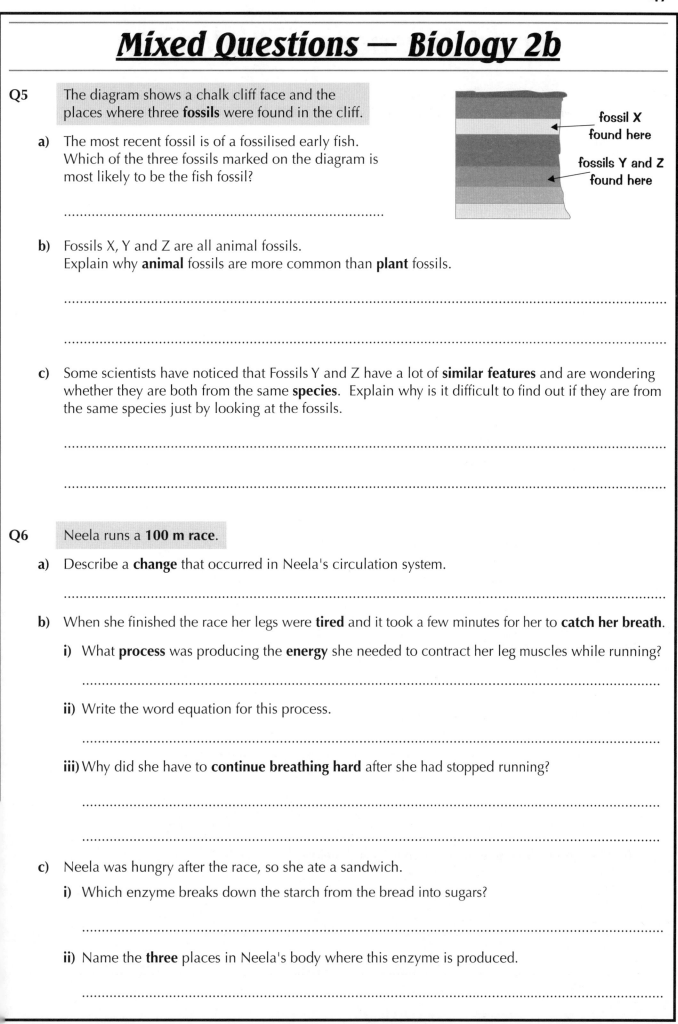

fossil **X** found here

fossils **Y** and **Z** found here

a) The most recent fossil is of a fossilised early fish. Which of the three fossils marked on the diagram is most likely to be the fish fossil?

....

b) Fossils X, Y and Z are all animal fossils. Explain why **animal** fossils are more common than **plant** fossils.

....

....

c) Some scientists have noticed that Fossils Y and Z have a lot of **similar features** and are wondering whether they are both from the same **species**. Explain why is it difficult to find out if they are from the same species just by looking at the fossils.

....

....

Q6 Neela runs a **100 m race**.

a) Describe a **change** that occurred in Neela's circulation system.

....

b) When she finished the race her legs were **tired** and it took a few minutes for her to **catch her breath**.

i) What **process** was producing the **energy** she needed to contract her leg muscles while running?

....

ii) Write the word equation for this process.

....

iii) Why did she have to **continue breathing hard** after she had stopped running?

....

....

c) Neela was hungry after the race, so she ate a sandwich.

i) Which enzyme breaks down the starch from the bread into sugars?

....

ii) Name the **three** places in Neela's body where this enzyme is produced.

....

Mixed Questions — Biology 2b

Q7 Sex determination in chickens is different from in humans. **Male** chickens (cockerels) have **two Z** chromosomes and **females** (hens) have **ZW** chromosomes.

a) What is a chromosome?

....

b) Apart from having different letters, explain how sex determination in chickens differs from humans.

....

Q8 One way that organisms **grow** is by making new cells by **mitosis**.

The graph shows how the amount of DNA per cell changes as a cell undergoes two cell divisions by mitosis. Point C on the graph is the time when the chromosomes first become visible in the new cells.

a) Describe and explain what is happening to the DNA during stage A.

....

....

b) What happens at time **B**?

....

c) i) What type of cells divide by mitosis?

....

ii) What type of reproduction uses mitosis?

....

d) Give **three differences** between mitosis and meiosis.

1. ....

2. ....

3. ....

Atoms, Compounds and Isotopes

Q1   **Complete** this table to show the relative masses of the particles in an atom.

Particle	Mass
Proton	1
	1
Electron	

Q2   Elements have a **mass number** and an **atomic number**.

a)   Circle the **mass number** on the diagram to the right.

$$^{12}_{\ 6}\text{C}$$

b)   What does the **mass number** of an element tell you about its atoms?

....

c)   What is the name for a substance that contains two
or more different elements chemically combined?

....

Q3   Choose the correct words from the list to **complete** this paragraph.

electrons	element	isotopes	protons	compound	neutrons

.... are different atomic forms of the same .... which have

the same number of .... but a different number of ....

Q4   Which of the following atoms are **isotopes** of each other? Explain your answer.

W $^{12}_{\ 6}\text{C}$ **X** $^{4}_{2}\text{He}$ **Y** $^{14}_{\ 6}\text{C}$ **Z** $^{14}_{\ 7}\text{N}$

Answer .... and ....

Explanation ....

....

Ionic Bonding

Q1 Tick the boxes to show whether the following statements are **true** or **false**.

True False

a) i) In ionic bonding, atoms lose or gain electrons. ☐ ☐

ii) Ions with opposite charges attract each other. ☐ ☐

iii) Atoms form ionic bonds to avoid having the same electronic structure as the noble gases. ☐ ☐

iv) Ionic bonds always produce giant ionic lattices. ☐ ☐

v) In ionic bonding, electrons from the inner shell are transferred. ☐ ☐

vi) Ionic compounds dissolve to form solutions that conduct electricity. ☐ ☐

b) Write out corrected versions of any **false** statements.

....

....

....

....

Q2 Magnesium (Group 2) and oxygen (Group 6) react to form **magnesium oxide**.

a) How many electrons does magnesium need to **lose** to get a full outer shell? ....

b) How many electrons does oxygen need to **gain** to get a full outer shell? ....

Q3 Sodium chloride (salt) has a **giant ionic structure**.

a) Circle the correct words from each pair to explain why sodium chloride has a **high melting point**.

> Sodium chloride has very **strong / weak** electrostatic forces of attraction
> between the **negative / positive** sodium ions and the **negative / positive**
> chlorine ions. These forces act in **one direction / all directions**.
> This means that it needs a **little / large** amount of energy to break the bonds.

b) Name two other **properties** of compounds with **giant ionic structures**.

1. ....

2. ....

Ionic Bonding

Q4   Diagrams can be used to represent the **structure** of chemical substances.

a)   Tick the correct box to show which of the following diagrams
could be used to represent the bonding in **sodium chloride**.

i)   **ii)**   **iii)**

☐   ☐   ☐

b)   Explain your answer to **a)**.

....

....

....

Q5   Mike conducts an experiment to find out if an **ionic compound** conducts electricity.
He tests the compound when it's solid, when it's dissolved in water and when it's molten.

a)   Complete the following table of results.

	Conducts electricity?
When solid	
When dissolved in water	
When molten	

b)   Explain your answers to part **a)**.

....

....

....

....

Top Tips: Giant ionic structures are the first of four different types of structure that you need to know about. You'll have to be able to identify the structure in different compounds later on — so make sure you can describe and recognise their properties now.

Ions and Formulas

Q1 Use the **diagram** to help you answer the following questions.

a) Which **group** of the periodic table does **sodium** belong to? ....

b) How many **electrons** does **chlorine** need to gain to get a full outer shell of electrons? ....

c) What is the **charge** on a **sodium ion**? ....

d) What is the chemical formula of **sodium chloride**? ....

Q2 Fill in the gaps in the paragraph below using words from the list.

1⁻ charge	2⁻ charge	negative	non-metals	1⁺ charge

Group 1 elements (the alkali metals) form ionic compounds with ....

where the metal ion has a .... Group 6 and 7 elements gain electrons

to form .... ions. For example, Group 7 elements (the halogens) form

ionic compounds with the alkali metals where the halide ion has a ....

Q3 Here are some elements and the ions they form:

beryllium, Be^{2+} potassium, K^+ iodine, I^- sulfur, S^{2-}

Make sure the charges on the ions balance.

Write down the formulas of four compounds which can be made using these elements.

1. ....   2. ....

3. ....   4. ....

Q4 Use information in the table to write out the **formulas** of the following compounds.

Positive Ions		Negative Ions	
Sodium	Na^+	Chloride	Cl^-
Potassium	K^+	Fluoride	F^-
Calcium	Ca^{2+}	Bromide	Br^-
Iron(II)	Fe^{2+}	Carbonate	CO_3^{2-}
Iron(III)	Fe^{3+}	Sulfate	SO_4^{2-}

a) potassium bromide ....

b) iron(II) chloride ....

c) calcium fluoride ....

Electronic Structure of Ions

Q1   Complete these diagrams to show the **electronic structure** and **charge** of the following ions. (The first one's been done for you.)

You can use the periodic table in the front of this book to help you.

a)

b)

c)

Q2   Calcium chloride is an **ionic** compound.

a) Write down the **formula** of calcium chloride. ....

b) Draw a diagram in the box below to represent the ionic bonding in calcium chloride. Show the **electronic structure** and **charges** of the ions.

Covalent Bonding

Q1   Indicate whether each statement is **true** or **false**.

                                                                  True   False

    a)   Covalent bonding involves sharing electrons.   ☐ ☐

    b)   Atoms react to gain a full outer shell of electrons.   ☐ ☐

    c)   Covalent bonding gives atoms the electronic structure of a noble gas.   ☐ ☐

    d)   Hydrogen can form two covalent bonds.   ☐ ☐

    e)   Carbon can form four covalent bonds.   ☐ ☐

Q2   **Complete** the following table to show how many electrons are needed to **fill up** the **outer shell** of these atoms.   *You can use a periodic table to help you with this.*

Atom	Carbon	Chlorine	Hydrogen	Nitrogen	Oxygen
Number of electrons needed to fill outer shell					

Q3   Why do some atoms **share** electrons?

....

....

Q4   Complete the following diagrams by adding the **electrons**. Only the outer shells are shown.

    a)   Hydrogen chloride (HCl)   **b)**   Oxygen (O_2)

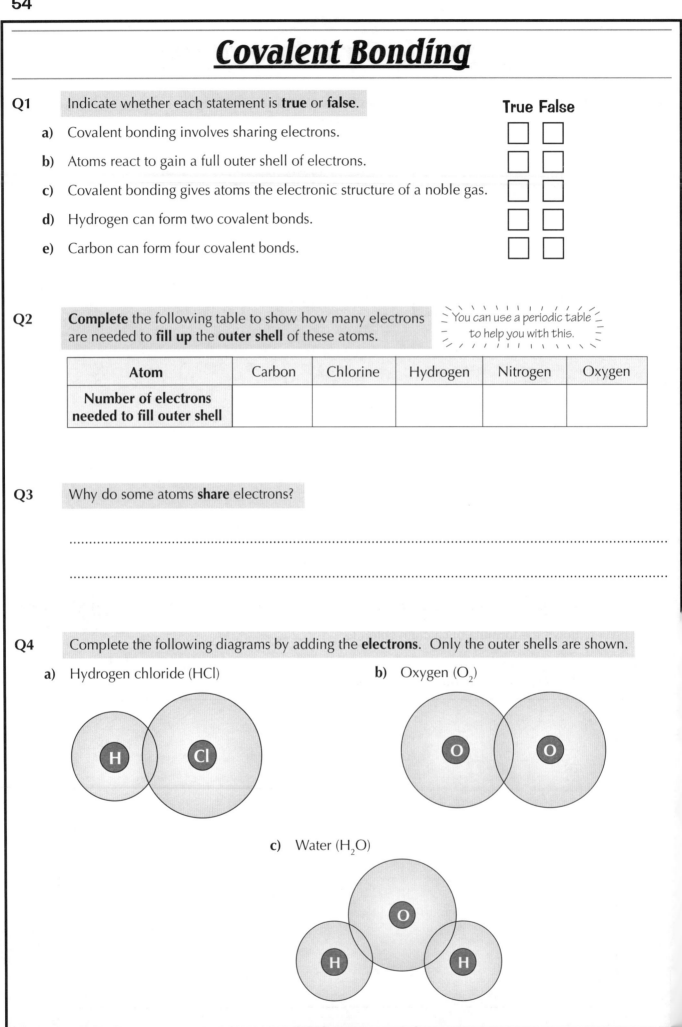

    c)   Water (H_2O)

Covalent Bonding

Q5 Add the outer shell **electrons** to the diagrams below.

a) Methane (CH$_4$)

b) Ammonia (NH$_3$)

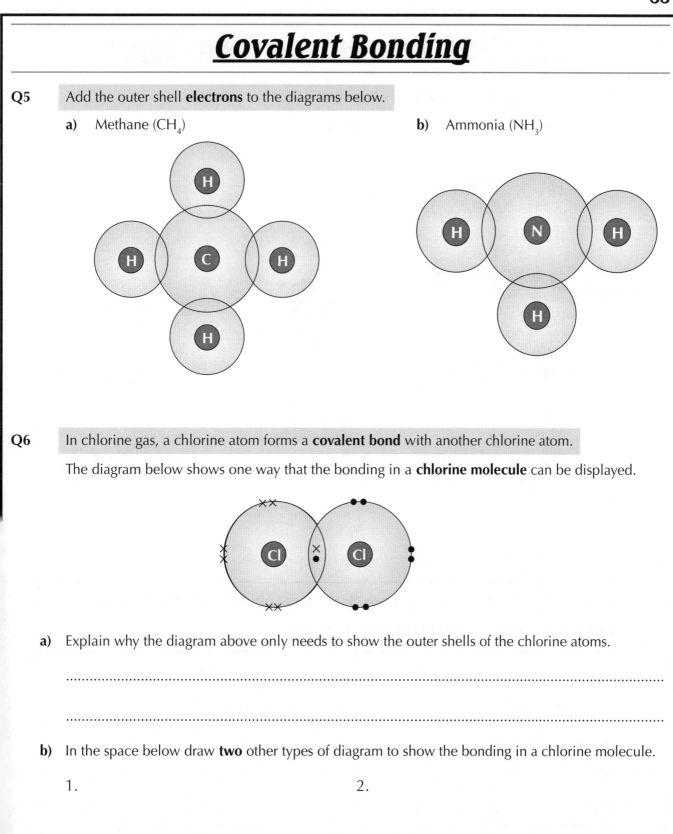

Q6 In chlorine gas, a chlorine atom forms a **covalent bond** with another chlorine atom.

The diagram below shows one way that the bonding in a **chlorine molecule** can be displayed.

a) Explain why the diagram above only needs to show the outer shells of the chlorine atoms.

....

....

b) In the space below draw **two** other types of diagram to show the bonding in a chlorine molecule.

1.   2.

Covalent Substances: Two Kinds

Q1   Which am I — **diamond**, **graphite** or **silicon dioxide**?

Match up the statements to the drawings below.

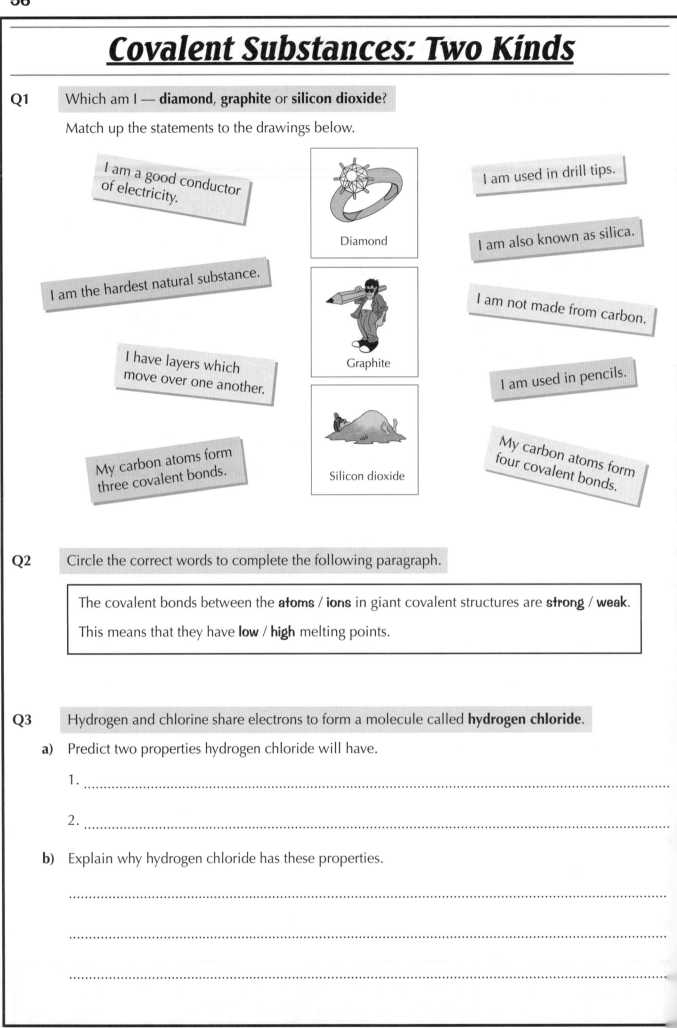

I am a good conductor of electricity.

I am the hardest natural substance.

I have layers which move over one another.

My carbon atoms form three covalent bonds.

Diamond

Graphite

Silicon dioxide

I am used in drill tips.

I am also known as silica.

I am not made from carbon.

I am used in pencils.

My carbon atoms form four covalent bonds.

Q2   Circle the correct words to complete the following paragraph.

> The covalent bonds between the **atoms** / **ions** in giant covalent structures are **strong** / **weak**.
>
> This means that they have **low** / **high** melting points.

Q3   Hydrogen and chlorine share electrons to form a molecule called **hydrogen chloride**.

a)   Predict two properties hydrogen chloride will have.

1. ....

2. ....

b)   Explain why hydrogen chloride has these properties.

....

....

....

Covalent Substances: Two Kinds

Q4   There are two types of **covalent substance**.

a) Name the **two** types of covalent substance.

1. ....

2. ....

b) Draw lines to match the following **covalent substances** to the diagrams.

| Graphite | Diamond | Silicon dioxide |

i)   ii)   iii)

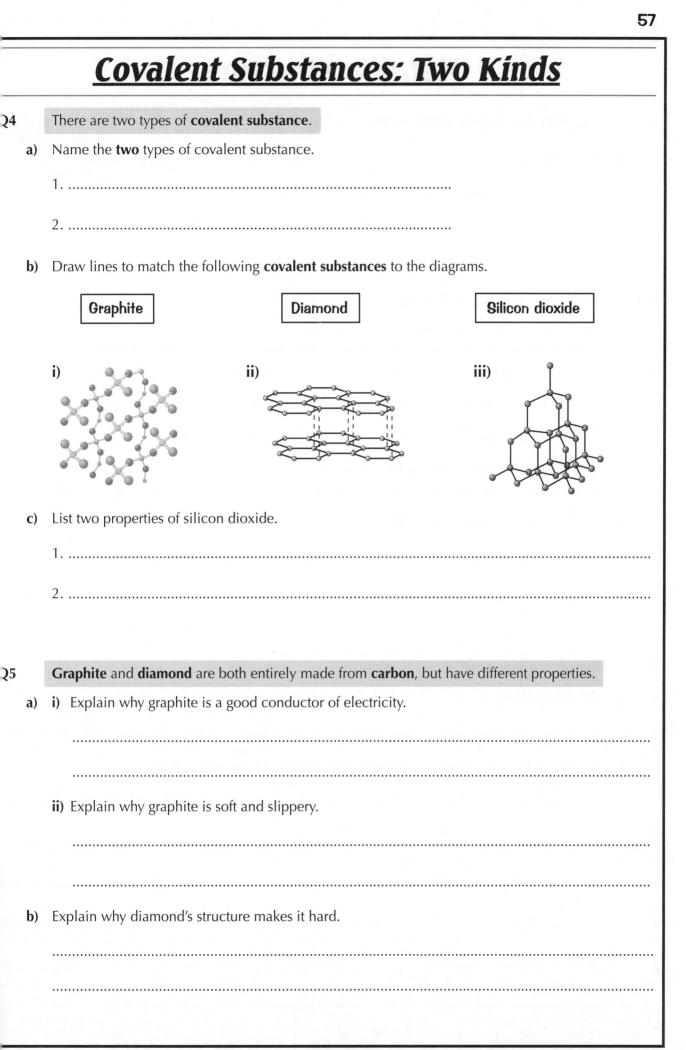

c) List two properties of silicon dioxide.

1. ....

2. ....

Q5   **Graphite** and **diamond** are both entirely made from **carbon**, but have different properties.

a) **i)** Explain why graphite is a good conductor of electricity.

....

....

ii) Explain why graphite is soft and slippery.

....

....

b) Explain why diamond's structure makes it hard.

....

....

Metallic Structures

Q1   **Complete** the following sentences about metals.

a)   Metals have a .... metallic structure.

b)   Metals are good conductors of .... and electricity.

c)   The .... in metals can slide over each other, so metals can be bent.

Q2   Metals consist of a **giant structure**.

a)   Circle the correct words from each pair in the passage below.

> Every metal atom in the structure provides one or more free **electrons** / **ions**
>
> from its **outer** / **inner** shell. There are **strong** / **weak** forces of electrostatic attraction
>
> between these and the **positive** / **negative** metal ions. This holds the metals atoms
>
> together in **a regular** / **an irregular** structure.

b)   How do metals **conduct electricity**?

....

....

Q3   Copper is a **pure metal**. Brass is an **alloy**.

a)   What is an alloy?

....

b)   Explain how the structures of copper and brass relate to how hard they are.

....

....

....

....

....

Metallic Structures

Q4   What type of **structure** is present in substances which: *Choose from giant ionic, giant covalent, simple molecular or giant metallic.*

a)   Don't conduct electricity when solid, but do when liquid. ....

b)   Have high melting points and don't conduct electricity when molten. ....

c)   Conduct electricity when solid and liquid. ....

Q5   Complete the following table by placing a **tick** or a **cross** in each box.

Property	Giant Ionic	Giant Covalent	Simple Molecular	Giant Metallic
High melting and boiling points				
Can conduct electricity when solid		except graphite		
Can conduct electricity when molten		except graphite		

Q6   The **properties** of four substances are given below.

Substance	Melting Point (°C)	Good Electrical Conductor?
A	2000	Only when molten or dissolved
B	2500	No
C	20	No
D	600	Yes

Identify the **structure** of each substance. Explain your choice.

a)   Substance A ....

....

b)   Substance B ....

....

c)   Substance C ....

....

d)   Substance D ....

....

New Materials

Q1 **Nitinol** is a smart material.

a) True or false?

                                                     True **False**

    i) Nitinol is a mixture of metals.   ☐   ☐

    ii) Nitinol is affected by light.   ☐   ☐

    iii) When cool, nitinol can bend and twist like rubber. ☐   ☐

b) Write out corrected versions of any **false** statements.

....

....

c) Explain why nitinol is sometimes called a 'shape memory alloy'.

....

....

d) Give one use of nitinol.

....

Q2 **Nanoparticles** are a new type of material.

a) Circle the correct words from each pair in the sentences below.

Nanoparticles contain roughly a few **hundred** / **thousand** atoms.

Nanoparticles have **identical** / **different** properties to the bulk material they are made from.

b) Explain why nanoparticles could help make new industrial **catalysts**.

....

....

Q3 Nanoparticles are really tiny particles, between 1 and 100 nanometres across.

How many nanometres are there in **1 mm**?

....

                                                                     1 nm =

....   0.000 001 mm

New Materials

Q4 There are different types of **nanoparticles**.

a) Choose from the words below to complete the paragraph.

molecules	shape memory alloys	atoms	fullerenes	hexagonal

Nanoparticles include .... These are ....

made from carbon atoms. The atoms are arranged in .... rings.

Different fullerenes contain different numbers of carbon ....

b) The **properties** of nanoparticles determine their use. Draw lines to match the properties and uses.

Lightweight but strong

Can detect specific molecules

Act like ball bearings to reduce friction

Lubricants for artificial joints

Building materials

Sensors to test water purity

c) What is the study of nanoparticles known as? Circle the correct word from the list below.

particle science   nanoscience   nanotubes   smart materials

d) Fullerenes are being developed for use in **medicine**.
They could be used to deliver **drugs** right into the cells where they are needed in the body.
Suggest what **property** fullerenes have that makes them suitable for this use.

....

....

Q5 Fullerenes can be joined together to make **nanotubes**.

a) Give a property of nanotubes that makes them useful as **electrical circuits** in computers.

....

b) Explain why nanotubes are often used to reinforce the graphite used to make **tennis rackets**.

....

....

Top Tips: Your old friend the examiner might ask you to evaluate the development and use of new materials. So, on the upside you can talk about how you can make weird and wonderful things with them. Then on the downside you can talk about the fact that, because they're so new, they could also have strange, scary properties that we haven't had time to find out about yet.

Polymers

Q1 **Polymer** molecules are **long chains**, as shown in the diagrams.

A   B

a) Which diagram shows a **thermosoftening** polymer? ....

b) Explain why **thermosetting** polymers don't melt when heated.

....

....

Q2 There are many different types of **polymers**.

Different polymers have different properties.
Give two factors that affect the properties of a polymer when it's made.

1. ....

2. ....

Q3 **High density polythene** and **low density polythene** have different properties.

The table compares some of their properties.

	DENSITY	SOFTENING TEMP.	FLEXIBILITY
LDP	Low	Below 100 °C	High
HDP	High	Above 100 °C	Fairly low

For each of the following applications choose which type of polythene should be used
and give a reason for your choice.

a) toothpaste tubes ....

....

b) freezer bags ....

....

c) hospital equipment that has to be sterilised ....

....

Relative Formula Mass

Q1 a) What is meant by the **relative atomic mass** of an element?

....

b) What are the **relative atomic masses (A$_r$)** of the following:

i) magnesium ....   **iv)** hydrogen ....   **vii)** K ....

ii) neon ....   **v)** C ....   **viii)** Ca ....

iii) oxygen ....   **vi)** Cu ....   **ix)** Cl ....

Q2 Use a periodic table to help identify the elements A, B and C.

> Element A has an A$_r$ of 4.
> Element B has an A$_r$ 3 times that of element A.
> Element C has an A$_r$ 4 times that of element A.

Element A is ....   Element B is ....

Element C is ....

Q3 a) Explain how the **relative formula mass** of a **compound** is calculated.

....

b) What are the **relative formula masses (M$_r$)** of the following:

i) water (H_2O) ....

ii) potassium hydroxide (KOH) ....

iii) nitric acid (HNO_3) ....

iv) sulfuric acid (H_2SO_4) ....

v) ammonium nitrate (NH_4NO_3) ....

Q4 The equation below shows a reaction between element X and water. The total M$_r$ of the products is **114**. What is substance X?

$$2X + 2H_2O \rightarrow 2XOH + H_2$$

....

....

Top Tips: The periodic table really comes in useful here. There's no way you'll be able to answer these questions without one (unless you've memorised all the elements' relative atomic masses — and that would just be silly). And lucky for you, you'll get given one in your exam. Yay!

Two Formula Mass Calculations

Q1 a) Write down the **formula** for calculating the **percentage mass** of an element in a compound.

b) Calculate the percentage mass of the following elements in ammonium nitrate, NH_4NO_3.

i) Nitrogen ....

ii) Hydrogen ....

iii) Oxygen ....

Q2 a) Calculate the percentage mass of **oxygen** in each of the following compounds.

A Fe_2O_3 **B** H_2O **C** $CaCO_3$

b) Which compound has the **greatest** percentage mass of oxygen? ....

Q3 **Nitrogen monoxide**, NO, reacts with oxygen, O_2, to form **oxide R**.

a) Calculate the percentage mass of nitrogen in **nitrogen monoxide**.

....

b) Oxide R has a percentage composition by mass of **30.4% nitrogen** and **69.6% oxygen**. Work out its empirical formula.

....

....

Q4 1.48 g of a **calcium compound** contains 0.8 g of calcium, 0.64 g of oxygen and 0.04 g of hydrogen.

Work out the empirical formula of the compound.

....

....

Calculating Masses in Reactions

Q1 Anna burns **10 g** of **magnesium** in air to produce **magnesium oxide** (MgO).

    a) Write out the **balanced equation** for this reaction.

....

    b) Calculate the mass of **magnesium oxide** that's produced.

....

....

....

Q2 What mass of **sodium** is needed to make **2 g** of **sodium oxide**?

Balanced Equation:

$$4Na + O_2 \rightarrow 2Na_2O$$

....

....

....

Q3 **Aluminium** and **iron oxide** (Fe_2O_3) react together to produce **aluminium oxide** (Al_2O_3) and **iron**.

    a) Write out the **balanced equation** for this reaction.

....

    b) What **mass** of iron is produced from **20 g** of iron oxide?

....

....

....

Q4 When heated, **limestone** ($CaCO_3$) decomposes to form **calcium oxide** (CaO) and **carbon dioxide**.

How many **kilograms** of limestone are needed to make **100 kilograms** of **calcium oxide**?

The calculation is exactly the same — just use 'kg' instead of 'g'.

....

....

....

....

Calculating Masses in Reactions

Q5   **Iron oxide** is reduced to **iron** inside a blast furnace using carbon. There are **three** stages involved.

Stage A	$C + O_2 \rightarrow CO_2$
Stage B	$CO_2 + C \rightarrow 2CO$
Stage C	$3CO + Fe_2O_3 \rightarrow 2Fe + 3CO_2$

a)   If **10 g** of **carbon** are used in stage B, and all the carbon monoxide produced gets used in stage C, what **mass** of CO_2 is produced in **stage C**?

....

....

....

....

Work out the mass of CO at the end of stage B first.

b)   Suggest how the CO_2 might be used after stage C.

....

Look at where CO_2 is used.

Q6   **Sodium sulfate** (Na_2SO_4) is made by reacting **sodium hydroxide** (NaOH) with **sulfuric acid** (H_2SO_4). **Water** is also produced.

a)   Write out the **balanced equation** for this reaction.

....

b)   What mass of **sodium hydroxide** is needed to make **75 g** of **sodium sulfate**?

....

....

....

....

c)   What mass of **water** is formed when **50 g** of **sulfuric acid** reacts?

....

....

....

....

Percentage Yield and Reversible Reactions

Q1 Aaliya and Natasha mixed together barium chloride ($BaCl_2$) and sodium sulfate (Na_2SO_4) solutions in a beaker. **Insoluble** barium sulfate was formed. They **filtered** the solution to obtain the solid substance, and then transferred the solid to a clean piece of **filter paper** and left it to dry.

a) Complete the following paragraph using the words provided.

percentage yield	lost	yield	lower	predicted	higher

The amount of product you get from a reaction is known as the ....

The more reactants you start with, the .... it will be.

The .... compares how much product you actually get to the

amount you ....

b) Aaliya calculated that they should produce a yield of **15 g** of barium sulfate. However, after completing the experiment they found they had only obtained **6 g**.

Calculate the **percentage yield** for this reaction.

....

....

c) Suggest **one** reason why their actual yield was lower than their predicted yield.

....

....

d) Explain how the following factors affect the percentage yield.

i) Reversible reactions ....

....

ii) Unexpected reactions ....

....

Q2 COP Chemicals makes **substance X** using a process that has a percentage yield of just **20%**.

The director of COP Chemicals doesn't think the **low percentage yield** is a problem because he is running his business at a **large profit**.
Suggest a reason why he should still try to **increase** the percentage yield of substance X.

....

....

Top Tips: Remember that a 100% yield simply doesn't happen in the big bad real world — your yield will always be somewhere between 0 and 100%. It's your job to remember why.

Chemical Analysis and Instrumental Methods

Q1 John did a **paper chromatography** experiment on sweet colourings. His results are shown below.

a) Write a brief method for this experiment, describing what John would have done.

....

....

....

....

Colour of Sweet	Distance Travelled by Dyes (mm)		
Brown	10	17	18
Red	18		
Green	10	17	
Orange	10	18	26
Blue	5	17	

b) How many dyes do the results indicate that the blue sweet contains? ....

c) Which sweet might contain the same mix of dyes as the red and green sweets together? Give a reason for your answer.

....

Q2 Forensic scientists use **instrumental methods** to analyse substances found at crime scenes.

a) Suspects in criminal cases can only be held for a short period of time without being charged. Suggest why instrumental methods are useful in these circumstances.

....

b) Give **two** other advantages of using instrumental methods.

1. ....

2. ....

Q3 Bob uses **gas chromatography** to separate a sample of a mixture of compounds.

a) The graph on the right is a **chromatograph** of his sample.

i) How many compounds are in the sample? ....

ii) Write down the **retention times** of the compounds.

....

b) What would linking the gas chromatography column to a **mass spectrometer** allow Bob to do?

....

....

Mixed Questions — Chemistry 2a

Q1 Three forms of the element **carbon** are shown in the diagrams below.

Key:
○ carbon atoms

R   S   T

a) i) **R** and **S** have the same type of structure. Write down the name of this type of structure.

....

ii) Explain why forms **R** and **S** have very high melting points.

....

....

b) i) Which of the above structures would you expect to be **less than 100 nanometers** across?

....

ii) What type of substance is this form of carbon?

....

Q2 Orwell found that 1.4 g of silicon reacted with 7.1 g of chlorine to produce the reactive liquid silicon chloride.

a) Work out the **empirical formula** of the silicon chloride.

....

....

b) Calculate the **percentage mass** of chlorine in silicon chloride.

....

....

c) Write down the balanced chemical equation for the reaction.

....

d) What mass of silicon chloride is produced when 1.4 g of silicon reacts with chlorine?

....

....

Mixed Questions — Chemistry 2a

Q3 The table gives data for some physical **properties** of a selection of elements and compounds.

substance	state at room temp	melting point / °C	boiling point / °C	electrical conductivity	
				solid	liquid
A	solid	114	184	poor	poor
B	gas	-73	-10	poor	poor
C	solid	3550	4827	poor	poor
D	solid	858	1505	poor	good
E	solid	1495	2870	good	good
F	liquid	0	50	poor	poor

a) Identify one substance that is **likely** to have a **simple molecular** structure. Justify your answer.

....

....

b) Which of the substances is **most likely** to have a **giant covalent** structure? ....

c) Explain why substance D is **unlikely** to be a **metallic** element.

....

Q4 There are different types of **polymers**.

Tick the boxes to show whether the following statements are true or false.

True False

a) Thermosoftening polymers have crosslinks. ☐ ☐

b) Thermosetting polymers consist of individual tangled chains of polymers. ☐ ☐

c) Thermosetting polymers don't soften when heated. ☐ ☐

Q5 **Magnesium** reacts with **nitric acid** (HNO_3) to form **magnesium nitrate** ($Mg(NO_3)_2$).

a) Work out the **relative formula mass** of magnesium nitrate.

....

b) The **mass of product** you expect to get in a reaction is known as the **predicted yield**. 12 g of magnesium is reacted with an excess of nitric acid. Work out the **predicted yield** of $Mg(NO_3)_2$.

....

....

c) In real life the **actual yield** is always less than the predicted yield. Give **one** reason why.

....

Mixed Questions — Chemistry 2a

Q6   Different types of substances have different **structures**.

a)   Draw lines to match the diagrams below to the type of substance.

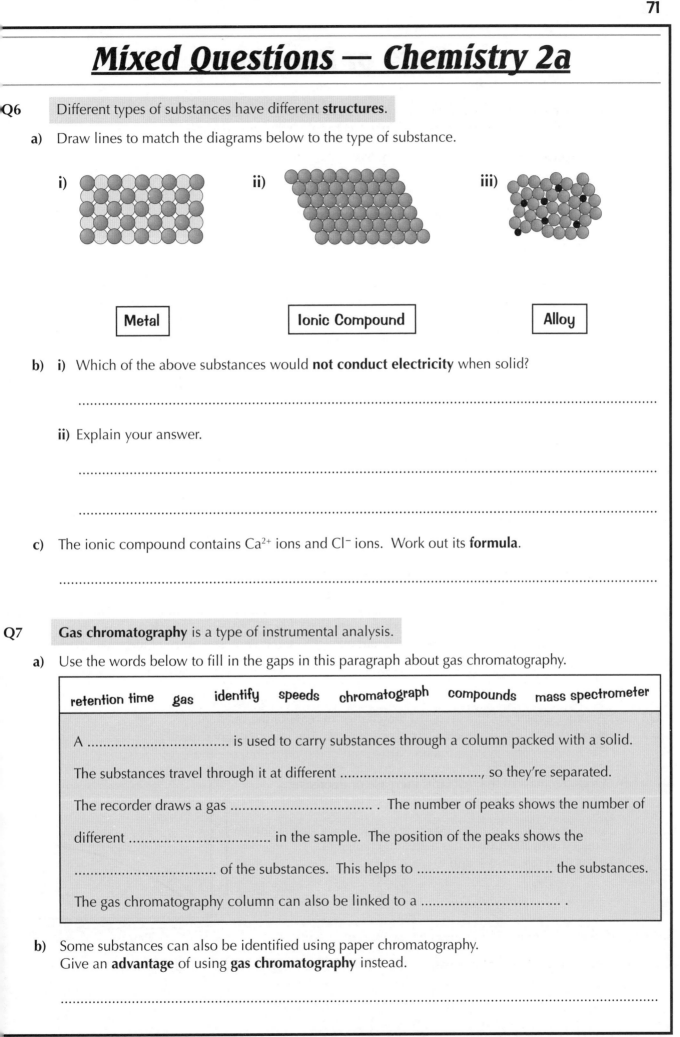

i)

ii)

iii)

| Metal | | Ionic Compound | | Alloy |

b)   i)   Which of the above substances would **not conduct electricity** when solid?

....

    ii)   Explain your answer.

....

....

c)   The ionic compound contains Ca^{2+} ions and Cl^- ions. Work out its **formula**.

....

Q7   **Gas chromatography** is a type of instrumental analysis.

a)   Use the words below to fill in the gaps in this paragraph about gas chromatography.

retention time   gas   identify   speeds   chromatograph   compounds   mass spectrometer

A .... is used to carry substances through a column packed with a solid.

The substances travel through it at different ...., so they're separated.

The recorder draws a gas .... The number of peaks shows the number of

different .... in the sample. The position of the peaks shows the

.... of the substances. This helps to .... the substances.

The gas chromatography column can also be linked to a ....

b)   Some substances can also be identified using paper chromatography.
Give an **advantage** of using **gas chromatography** instead.

....

Rate of Reaction

Q1   The four statements below are about **rate of reaction**.
Circle the correct words from each pair to complete the sentences.

a)   The **higher** / **lower** the temperature the faster the rate of reaction.

b)   A **higher** / **lower** concentration or pressure will reduce the rate of reaction.

c)   A smaller surface area **increases** / **decreases** the rate of reaction.

d)   A catalyst **does** / **doesn't** change the rate of reaction.

Q2   In an experiment, **different sizes** of marble chips were reacted with excess hydrochloric acid.
The **same mass** of marble was used each time. The graph below shows how much **gas** was
produced with large marble chips (X), medium marble chips (Y) and small marble chips (Z).

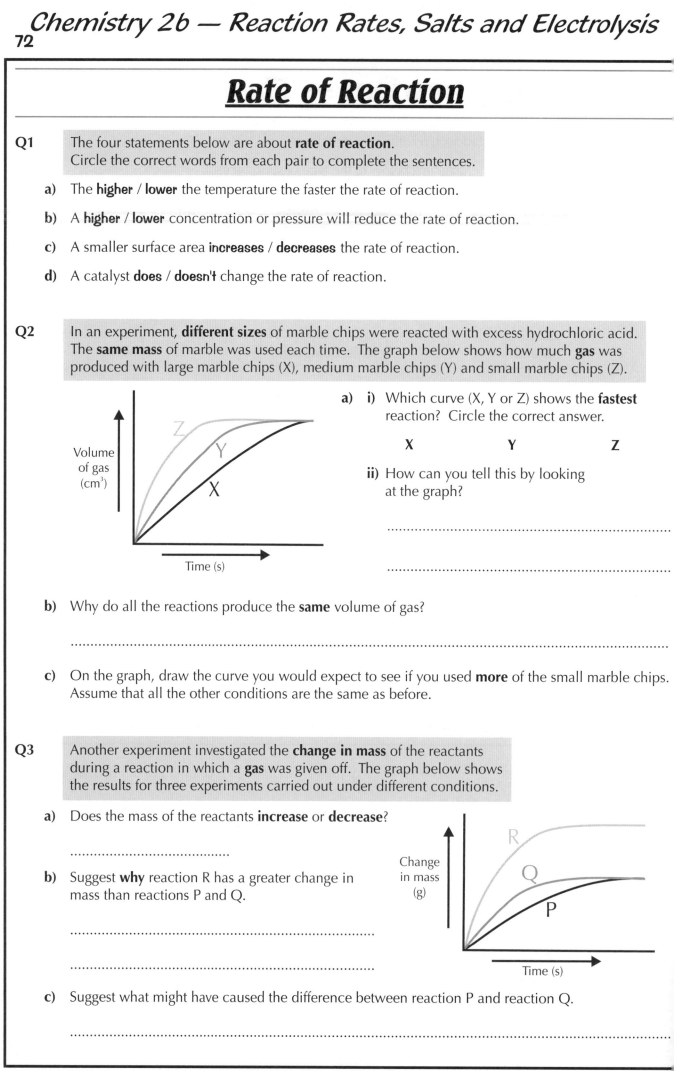

a)   i)   Which curve (X, Y or Z) shows the **fastest**
reaction? Circle the correct answer.

X   Y   Z

ii) How can you tell this by looking
at the graph?

....

....

b)   Why do all the reactions produce the **same** volume of gas?

....

c)   On the graph, draw the curve you would expect to see if you used **more** of the small marble chips.
Assume that all the other conditions are the same as before.

Q3   Another experiment investigated the **change in mass** of the reactants
during a reaction in which a **gas** was given off. The graph below shows
the results for three experiments carried out under different conditions.

a)   Does the mass of the reactants **increase** or **decrease**?

....

b)   Suggest **why** reaction R has a greater change in
mass than reactions P and Q.

....

....

c)   Suggest what might have caused the difference between reaction P and reaction Q.

....

Measuring Rates of Reaction

Q1 Use the words provided to complete the sentences below about measuring rates of reaction.

faster	rate	volume	reactants	gas	mass	formed	precipitation

The .... of a reaction can be measured by observing either how quickly

the .... are used up or how quickly the products are ....

In a .... reaction you usually measure how quickly the product is formed.
The product turns the solution cloudy. The .... it turns cloudy the quicker
the reaction.

In a reaction that produces a .... you can measure how quickly the

.... of the reactants changes or measure the .... of

gas given off in a certain time interval.

Q2 Sam conducted an experiment with equal masses of marble chips and equal
volumes of hydrochloric acid (HCl). He used two **different concentrations** of acid
and measured the **change in mass** of the reactants. Below is a graph of the results.

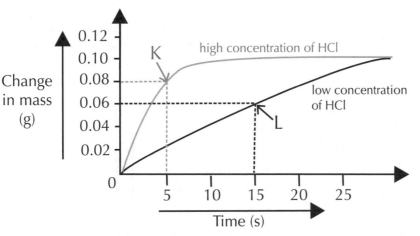

a) **Circle** the letter(s) to show the **valid conclusion(s)** you might draw from this graph.

  A Rate of reaction depends on the temperature of the reactants.

  B Increasing the concentration of the acid has no effect on the rate of reaction.

  C Rate of reaction depends on the acid concentration.

  D Rate of reaction depends on the mass of the marble chips.

b) **Calculate** the rate of reaction at points K and L on the graph.

  i) Rate at point K .... *Don't forget the units.*

  ii) Rate at point L ....

Measuring Rates of Reaction

Q3 Charlie was comparing the rate of reaction of 5 g of magnesium ribbon with 20 ml of **five different concentrations** of hydrochloric acid. Each time he measured how much **gas** was produced during the **first minute** of the reaction. He did the experiment **twice** for each concentration of acid and obtained these results:

Concentration of HCl (mol/dm^3)	Experiment 1 — volume of gas produced (cm^3)	Experiment 2 — volume of gas produced (cm^3)	Average volume of gas produced (cm^3)
2	92	96	
1.5	63	65	
1	44	47	
0.5	20	50	
0.25	9	9	

a) **Fill in** the last column of the table.

b) Circle the **anomalous** result in the table.

The anomalous result is the one that doesn't seem to fit in.

c) Which concentration of hydrochloric acid produced the fastest rate of reaction? ....

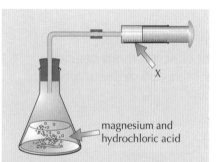

magnesium and hydrochloric acid

d) A diagram of the **apparatus** used in the experiment is shown on the left.

   i) What is the object marked **X** called?

   ....

   ii) Name one other key piece of apparatus needed for this experiment that is not shown in the diagram.

   ....

e) **Sketch** a graph of the average volume of gas produced from this investigation against concentration of HCl and **label** the axes. Do not include the anomalous result.

You don't need to plot the values, just draw what the graph would look like.

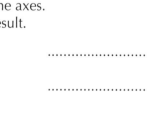

....

....

....

f) Why did Charlie do the experiment twice and calculate the average volume?

....

g) How might the **anomalous** result have come about?

....

Rate of Reaction Experiments

Q1   Choose from the words below to complete the paragraph.

smaller	larger	slower	react	decrease	faster	increase

When you crush up a large solid into powder, you .... its surface area.

This means it reacts .... Large lumps have a

.... surface area so they .... more slowly.

Q2   Matilda conducted an experiment to investigate the effect of **surface area** on rate of reaction. She added dilute hydrochloric acid to **large marble chips** and measured the volume of gas produced at regular time intervals. She repeated the experiment using the same mass of **powdered marble**. Below is a graph of her results.

a) Which curve, A or B, was obtained when **large pieces** of marble were used?

....

b) On the graph opposite, draw the curve you would get if you used the **same mass** of **medium** sized marble pieces. Label it C.

Volume of gas (cm^3)

A

B

Time (s)

c) Name the **independent** variable in this investigation.

....

d) Is there enough information given above for you to be sure whether this was a **fair test** or not? Explain your answer.

....

....

....

e) Which other method(s) could you use to measure the rate of this reaction? Tick the correct one(s).

☐	Timing how long the reaction takes to go cloudy.
☐	Timing how long the reaction takes to start.
☐	Measuring how quickly the reaction loses mass.

Rate of Reaction Experiments

Q3   Dillon investigated the reaction between **magnesium** and excess **hydrochloric acid**. He did the experiment using **different concentrations** of acid. He recorded the mass of the reactants at the start and at every 10 seconds for 2 minutes and calculated the change in mass for each reading.

a)   How many readings did he take for each concentration? ....

b)   Suggest the labels (including units) that he might use for a graph of his results:

   x-axis ....

   y-axis ....

c)   On the axes to the right, draw and label sketches of the curves you would expect for a **high** and a **low** concentration of acid.

d)   Here is one of Dillon's results:

   > original mass of reactants: 145.73 g
   >
   > mass of reactants at 1 minute 40 seconds: 143.89 g

   Don't forget to include the units.

   Calculate the **change** in mass ....

Q4   Here is a graph which has been obtained from a rate of reaction investigation.

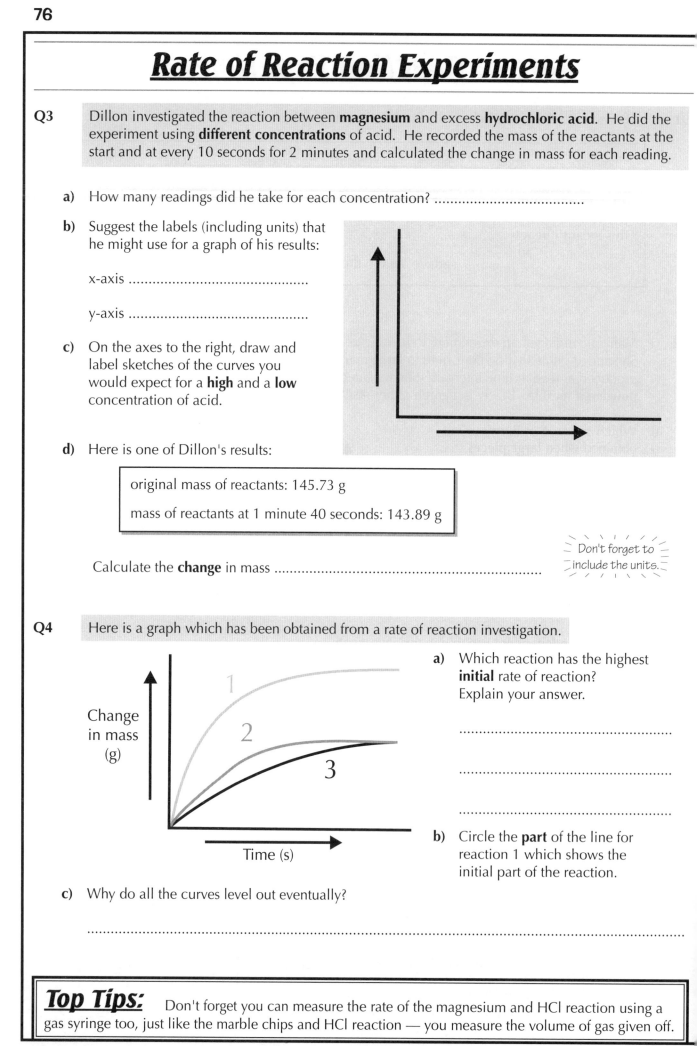

a)   Which reaction has the highest **initial** rate of reaction? Explain your answer.

   ....

   ....

   ....

b)   Circle the **part** of the line for reaction 1 which shows the initial part of the reaction.

c)   Why do all the curves level out eventually?

   ....

Top Tips: Don't forget you can measure the rate of the magnesium and HCl reaction using a gas syringe too, just like the marble chips and HCl reaction — you measure the volume of gas given off.

Chemistry 2b — Reaction Rates, Salts and Electrolysis

Rate of Reaction Experiments

Q5 When you mix **sodium thiosulfate** solution and **hydrochloric acid**, a precipitate is formed. Underline the correct statement(s) about the reaction.

The precipitate is white.

The mixture goes cloudy.

Sulfur is yellow.

Q6 Yasmin investigates the effect of **temperature** on the rate of the reaction between sodium thiosulfate solution and hydrochloric acid. She mixes the reactants together in a flask and times how long a cross placed under the flask takes to disappear.

a) Circle the items from the following list that she could use to do this.

| scales | syringe | water bath | stopclock | thermometer |

b) Here are some results from her investigation:

Temperature (°C)	20	30	40	50	60
Time taken for cross to disappear (s)	201	177		112	82

   i) As the temperature increases, does the reaction get **faster** or **slower**? ....

   ii) One of the values in the table is missing. Circle the most likely value for it from the list below.

   145 s   **192 s**   **115 s**

c) i) Name the **independent** variable in this experiment. ....

   ii) Name the **dependent** variable in this experiment. ....

d) Suggest one thing Yasmin could do to make her results more **reliable**.

   ....

   ....

Q7 Nir uses the sodium thiosulfate and hydrochloric acid reaction to investigate the effect of varying the **concentration** of hydrochloric acid on the rate of reaction. He mixes the reactants together in a flask and times how long it takes for a cross placed under the flask to disappear.

He obtains these results:

Concentration of HCl (mol/dm³)	2.00	1.75	1.50	1.25	1.00
Time taken for cross to disappear (s)	13	23	38	50	67

What conclusion can Nir draw from these results?

....

Rate of Reaction Experiments

Q8   Hydrogen peroxide **decomposes** into water and oxygen.

a)   Complete the equation for the decomposition of hydrogen peroxide.

$$2H_2O_2 \rightleftharpoons \text{...............} + O_2$$

Don't forget it needs to be balanced.

b)   What is a good way to measure the rate of this reaction?
Circle the letter next to the correct answer.

A   Weigh the amount of water produced

B   Time how long the reaction takes to go cloudy

C   Measure the volume of gas produced at regular time intervals

D   Measure the temperature

c)   Circle the correct word from the pair to complete the sentence.

We can **increase** / **decrease** the speed of this decomposition reaction by using a catalyst.

Q9   The decomposition of hydrogen peroxide can be used to investigate the effect of a **catalyst** on the rate of reaction. A student compared three different catalysts to see which was the most effective (increased the rate of reaction the most). He used a gas syringe to measure the amount of gas produced. Below is a graph of his results.

a)   Label the y-axis (don't forget to include appropriate units).

b)   The three catalysts used in this experiment were **potato peel**, **blood** and **manganese (IV) oxide**. Manganese (IV) oxide is the most effective catalyst for this reaction.

....

....

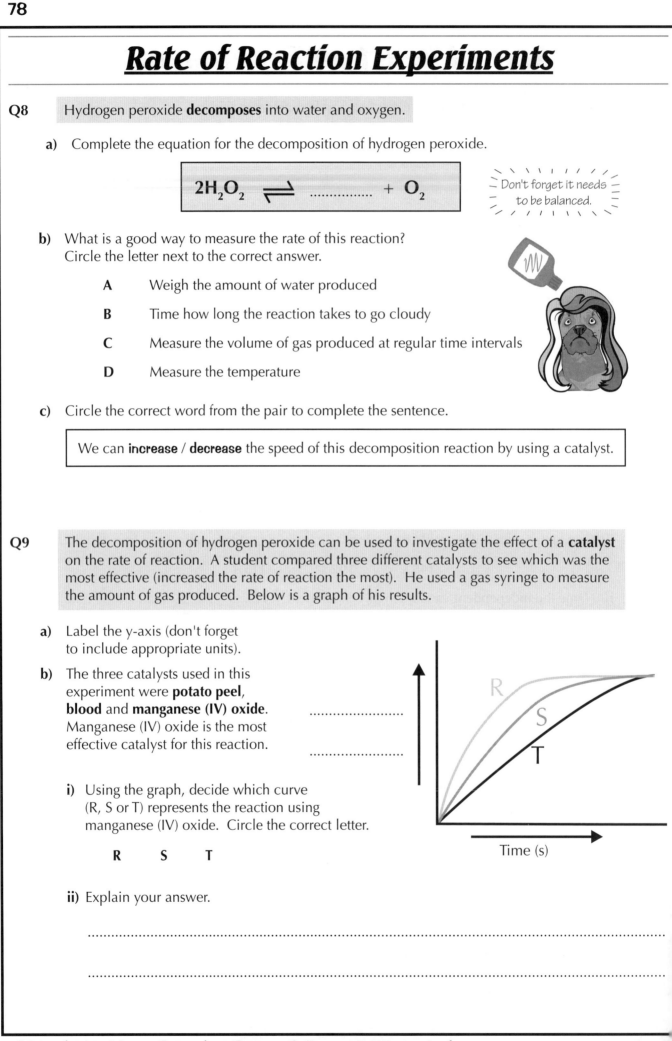

i)   Using the graph, decide which curve (R, S or T) represents the reaction using manganese (IV) oxide. Circle the correct letter.

R   **S**   **T**

ii) Explain your answer.

....

....

Collision Theory

Q1   Draw lines to match up the changes with their effects.

increasing the temperature

means fewer particles of reactant are present, so less frequent collisions occur

decreasing the concentration

gives particles a bigger area of solid reactant to react with

increasing the surface area

makes the particles move faster, so they collide more often

Q2   Circle the correct words to complete the following sentences.

a)   If you heat up a reaction, you give the particles more **energy** / **surface area**.

b)   This makes them move **faster** / **slower** so successful collisions happen **more** / **less** frequently.

c)   So, increasing the temperature increases the **concentration** / **rate of reaction**.

Q3   Gases are always under **pressure**.

a)   **i)** If you increase the pressure of a gas reaction, does the rate **increase** or **decrease**?

....

  ii) Explain your answer.

....

....

b)   In the boxes on the right draw two diagrams — one showing particles of two different gases at low pressure, the other showing the same two gases at high pressure.

low pressure   **high pressure**

Q4   Read the four statements about **surface area** and rate of reaction.
Tick the appropriate boxes to show whether they are true or false.

True False

a)   Breaking a larger solid into smaller pieces decreases its surface area. ☐ ☐

b)   A larger surface area will mean a faster rate of reaction. ☐ ☐

c)   A larger surface area decreases how often successful collisions happen. ☐ ☐

d)   Powdered marble has a larger surface area than an equal mass of marble chips has. ☐ ☐

Collision Theory and Catalysts

Q1   What is meant by **activation energy**?

....

....

Q2   **Catalysts** are often used in reactions.

a)   What is a catalyst?

....

....

b)   The diagram to the right shows two reactions, A and B.
One has a catalyst and one doesn't.

      i) Which line shows the reaction
with a catalyst, A or B?

      ....

      ii) Explain your answer.

      ....

      ....

Q3   Catalysts are used in many **industrial reactions**.

a)   Give **one** reason why catalysts are **useful** for industrial processes.

....

....

b)   Give **two** possible **problems** with using catalysts in industrial processes.

    1. ....

    2. ....

c)   Name an industrial process and the catalyst it uses.

....

Top Tips: Unlike other exciting things, such as chocolate buttons and a fashion for sparkly leggings, a catalyst isn't used up or changed — so you can use it again and again... and again.

Energy Transfer in Reactions

Q1 Circle the correct words from each pair in this paragraph about **exothermic** reactions.

> Exothermic reactions transfer energy **to** / **from** the surroundings, usually in the form of **heat** / **sound**. This is often shown by a **fall** / **rise** in **temperature** / **mass**.

Q2 Three examples of exothermic reactions are **burning fuels**, **neutralisation** and **oxidation**.

a) Write **B** for burning fuel or **N** for neutralisation reaction next to each of the following reactions.

☐ acid + alkali → salt + water

☐ petrol + oxygen → carbon dioxide + water

b) Give another word for 'burning'. ....

c) Give an example of an oxidation reaction.

....

Q3 Fill in the missing words in this paragraph about **endothermic** reactions.

> Endothermic reactions .... energy from the surroundings,
> usually in the form of ....
> This is often shown by a .... in temperature.

Q4 Limestone ($CaCO_3$) breaks down when heated to form quicklime and carbon dioxide.

a) What type of reaction is this?

....

b) The reaction requires a large amount of heat.

i) Is it **exothermic** or **endothermic**? ....

ii) Explain your answer ....

c) Breaking down 1 tonne (1000 kg) of $CaCO_3$ requires about 1 800 000 kJ of heat energy.

i) How much heat energy would be needed to make **1 kg** of $CaCO_3$ break down?

....

ii) How much $CaCO_3$ could be broken down by **90 000 kJ** of heat energy?

....

Energy Transfer in Reactions

Q5 Sam did an experiment to investigate the **thermal decomposition** of **copper sulfate**. He wrote this about his investigation:

> "When I heated up blue copper sulfate it steamed and went white. After it cooled down I dropped a little water on it and it got really hot and turned blue again".

Water vapour

Answer these questions about Sam's observations:

a) Which part of Sam's experiment was exothermic? ....

b) Which part of Sam's experiment was endothermic? ....

c) Is blue copper sulfate **anhydrous** or **hydrated**? Circle the correct answer.

anhydrous

hydrated

Anhydrous means without water and hydrated means containing water.

d) Write a **word equation** for this reaction in the box below.

....
⇌
.... + ...

e) What is a reaction that can go both ways called?

....

Q6 Here are some practical uses of chemical reactions. Decide whether each reaction is endothermic or exothermic. In the box, put **N** for endothermic and **X** for exothermic.

a) A camping stove burns methylated spirit to heat a pan of beans. ☐

b) Special chemical cool packs are used by athletes to treat injuries. They take heat in and the pack becomes very cold. ☐

c) Self-heating cans of coffee contain chemicals in the base. When the chemicals are combined they produce heat which warms the can. ☐

d) Baking powder is used to make cakes rise. When it's heated in the oven it thermally decomposes to produce a gas. ☐

Top Tips: Anything that takes heat in is endothermic. Endothermic reactions are pretty rare in everyday life but they do occur — think about cooking eggs or even melting ice cream in your mouth.

Acids and Alkalis

Q1 a) Complete the equation below for the reaction between an acid and a base.

acid + base $\rightarrow$ .... + ...

b) Circle the correct term for this kind of reaction.

decomposition **oxidation** **neutralisation**

c) Which of the following ions:

$$H^+_{(aq)} \quad OH^-_{(aq)} \quad Cl^-_{(aq)} \quad Na^+_{(aq)}$$

i) react with each other to form water? ....

ii) is present in an acidic solution? ....

iii) is present in an alkaline solution? ....

iv) would be present in a solution with a pH of 10? ....

v) would be present in a solution with a pH of 2? ....

Q2 Complete the following sentences.

a) Solutions which are not acidic or alkaline are said to be ....

b) An example of an indicator is ....

c) If a substance is neutral it has a pH of ....

d) A soluble base is known as an ....

Q3 Joey wanted to make **sodium chloride** (a salt) by adding hydrochloric acid to sodium hydroxide solution.

a) Complete the **symbol equation** below for this reaction.

$HCl_{(aq)}$ + $NaOH_{(aq)}$ $\rightarrow$ .... + ...

b) Write an equation to show the reaction between hydrogen ions and hydroxide ions in this reaction.

....

c) Suggest what Joey could use to tell whether the reaction was **over**.

....

d) What would the pH of the products be?

....

Acids and Alkalis

Q4 State symbols give the **physical state** of a substance.

Give the **symbols** for the following states.

a) Solid

b) Liquid

c) Gas

d) Dissolved in water (aqueous)

Q5 Ants' stings hurt because of the **formic acid** they release.

a) The table to the right shows the pH measurements of some household substances. Suggest a substance from the list that could be used to relieve the discomfort of an ant sting.

....

b) Explain your answer.

....

....

....

Substance	pH
lemon juice	4
baking soda	9
caustic soda	14
soap powder	11

Q6 Joey wanted to test whether some antacid tablets really do **neutralise acid**.

He added a tablet to some hydrochloric acid, stirred it until it dissolved and tested the pH of the solution. He carried out further tests after dissolving a second, third and fourth tablet. His results are shown in the table below.

Number of Tablets	pH
0	1
1	2
2	3
3	7
4	9

a) Plot a graph of the results.

b) Describe how the pH changes when antacid tablets are added to the acid.

....

c) How many tablets were needed to neutralise the acid? ....

Top Tips: State symbols might look like an afterthought but they provide pretty important information about a reaction. You need to know whether your products are going to be liquids that you can contain in a flask, or gases that'll need a bung to stop them floating off around the room.

Acids Reacting With Metals

Q1   The diagram below shows **aluminium** reacting with **sulfuric acid**.

a)   Label the diagram with the names of the chemicals.

....

....

....

b)   Complete the word equation for this reaction:

aluminium + ... → **aluminium sulfate** + ...

c)   Write a balanced symbol equation for this reaction.

....

The formula of aluminium sulfate is $Al_2(SO_4)_3$.

d)   Zinc also reacts with sulfuric acid. Give the word equation for this reaction.

....

e)   Write a balanced symbol equation for the reaction between magnesium and hydrochloric acid.

....

Q2   The table shows what happens when different **metals** react with **hydrochloric acid**.

Metal	A	B	C	D
Observations	gas bubbles formed vigorously / metal disappeared quickly	no gas bubbles formed / metal unaffected by the acid	gas bubbles form slowly / most of the metal remained after 5 min	gas bubbles form steadily / most of the metal disappeared after 5 min

a)   Which of A-D is the **most** reactive metal? ....

b)   Which of metals A-D are **less** reactive than hydrogen? ....

c)   The metals used in this experiment were **magnesium**, **zinc**, **iron** and **copper**.
Using the reactivity series on the right to help you, match each of these
metals to the correct letter from the table.

A ....   C ....

B ....   D ....

most reactive

magnesium

zinc

iron

hydrogen

copper

least reactive

Acids Reacting With Metals

Q3   Rhiannon is planning an experiment to investigate the rate of reaction between magnesium and different **concentrations** of hydrochloric acid.

a)   How could she measure the rate of the reaction?

....

b)   What is the **independent variable** in her experiment?

....

c)   Give two variables that she will need to keep the **same** in her experiment.

....

Q4   Fill in the blanks using some of the words given below.

reactive	copper	nitric	more	hydrogen	less	chloride
sulfuric	carbon dioxide		non-metals	nitrate	metals	

Acids react with most .... to form salts and .... gas.

Metals like .... and silver which are less .... than

hydrogen don't react with acids. The .... reactive the metal, the more

vigorously the bubbles of gas form. Hydrochloric acid forms .... salts

and .... acid produces sulfate salts. However, the reactions of metals

with .... acid don't follow this simple pattern.

Q5 a)   Write out the **balanced** versions of the following equations.

i) $Ca + HCl \rightarrow CaCl_2 + H_2$ ....

ii) $Na + HCl \rightarrow NaCl + H_2$ ....

iii) $Li + H_2SO_4 \rightarrow Li_2SO_4 + H_2$ ....

b)   Hydrobromic acid reacts with magnesium as shown in the equation below to form a bromide salt and hydrogen.

$$Mg + 2HBr \rightarrow MgBr_2 + H_2$$

i) Name the salt formed in this reaction. ....

ii) Write a balanced symbol equation for the reaction between aluminium and hydrobromic acid. (The formula of aluminium bromide is $AlBr_3$.)

....

Oxides, Hydroxides and Ammonia

Q1 Fill in the blanks to complete the word equations for **acids** reacting with **metal oxides** and **metal hydroxides**.

a) hydrochloric acid + lead oxide → .... chloride + water

b) nitric acid + copper hydroxide → copper .... + water

c) sulfuric acid + zinc oxide → zinc sulfate + ...

d) hydrochloric acid + ... oxide → nickel .... + ...

e) .... acid + copper oxide → .... nitrate + ...

f) sulfuric acid + ... hydroxide → sodium .... + ...

Q2 a) Put a tick in the box next to any of the sentences below which are **true**.

Alkalis are bases which don't dissolve in water.

Acids react with metal oxides to form a salt and water.

Hydrogen gas is formed when an acid reacts with an alkali.

Salts and water are formed when acids react with metal hydroxides.

Ammonia solution is alkaline.

Calcium hydroxide is an acid that dissolves in water.

b) Use the formulas below to write **symbol equations** for two acid/base reactions.

H_2SO_4 H_2O CuO H_2O $NaCl$ $CuSO_4$ HCl $NaOH$

....

....

Q3 Name two substances which would react to make each of the following **salts**.

a) Potassium sulfate ....

b) Ammonium chloride ....

c) Silver nitrate ....

Oxides, Hydroxides and Ammonia

Q4 Ammonia can be neutralised by **nitric acid** to form a salt.

a) Underline the correct formula for ammonia below.

NH_4NO_3 $\qquad\qquad$ NH_4Cl $\qquad\qquad$ NH_3 $\qquad\qquad$ NH_2 $\qquad\qquad$ NH_4

b) Fill in the blanks in the passage below using some of the words from the list.

proteins $\quad$ solid $\quad$ fertilisers $\quad$ acidic $\quad$ nitrogen $\quad$ liquid $\quad$ salts $\quad$ alkaline
Ammonia dissolves in water to form an .... solution. Ammonia contains .... which plants need to produce ...., so it is used to make ammonium .... which are widely used as ....

c) Write down the word equation for making **ammonium nitrate**.

....

d) Why is ammonium nitrate a particularly good fertiliser?

....

e) How is this neutralisation reaction different from most neutralisation reactions?

....

Q5 **a)** Complete the following equations.

i) $H_2SO_{4(aq)}$ + ... $\rightarrow$ $CuSO_{4(aq)}$ + $H_2O_{(l)}$

ii) $2HNO_{3(aq)}$ + $MgO_{(s)}$ $\rightarrow$ $Mg(NO_3)_{2(aq)}$ + ...

iii) .... + $KOH_{(aq)}$ $\rightarrow$ $KCl_{(aq)}$ + $H_2O_{(l)}$

iv) $2HCl_{(aq)}$ + ... $\rightarrow$ $ZnCl_{2(aq)}$ + $H_2O_{(l)}$

v) $H_2SO_{4(aq)}$ + $2NaOH_{(aq)}$ $\rightarrow$ .... + ...

b) **Balance** the following acid/base reactions.

i) $\quad$ NaOH $\:+\:$ H_2SO_4 $\rightarrow$ Na_2SO_4 $+$ H_2O

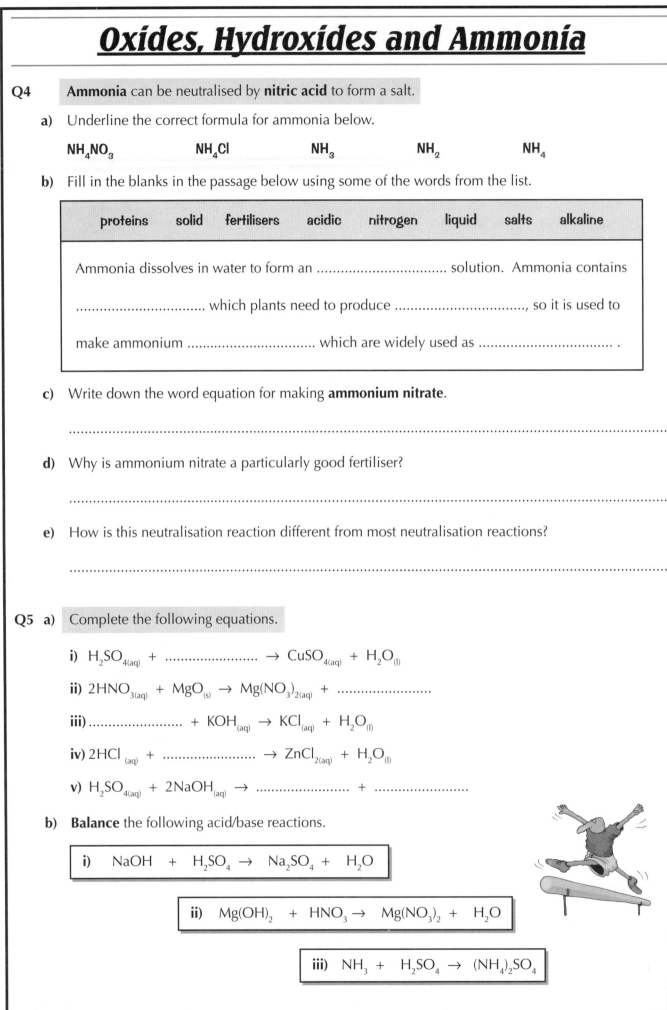

ii) $\quad$ $Mg(OH)_2$ $\:+\:$ HNO_3 $\rightarrow$ $Mg(NO_3)_2$ $+$ H_2O

iii) $\:$ NH_3 $\:+\:$ H_2SO_4 $\rightarrow$ $(NH_4)_2SO_4$

Making Salts

Q1 Complete the following sentences by circling the correct word from each pair.

a) Most chlorides, sulfates and nitrates are **soluble** / **insoluble** in water.

b) Most oxides and hydroxides are **soluble** / **insoluble** in water.

c) Soluble salts can be made by reacting **acids** / **alkalis** with insoluble bases until they are just **neutralised** / **displaced**.

d) Insoluble salts are made by **precipitation** / **electrolysis**.

Q2 **A**, **B** and **C** are symbol equations for reactions in which **salts** are formed.

$$A \qquad CuO_{(s)} + H_2SO_{4(aq)} \rightarrow CuSO_{4(aq)} + H_2O_{(l)}$$

$$B \qquad 2NaOH_{(aq)} + H_2SO_{4(aq)} \rightarrow Na_2SO_{4(aq)} + 2H_2O_{(l)}$$

$$C \qquad Pb(NO_3)_{2(aq)} + H_2SO_{4(aq)} \rightarrow PbSO_{4(s)} + 2HNO_{3(aq)}$$

Which equation (A, B, C) refers to the formation of a salt:

a) in an acid/alkali reaction ....

b) by precipitation ....

c) from an insoluble base ....

Q3 **Silver chloride** is an insoluble salt which is formed as a **precipitate** when silver nitrate and sodium chloride solutions are mixed together.

a) Complete the word equation for the reaction.

.... + ... → silver chloride + ...

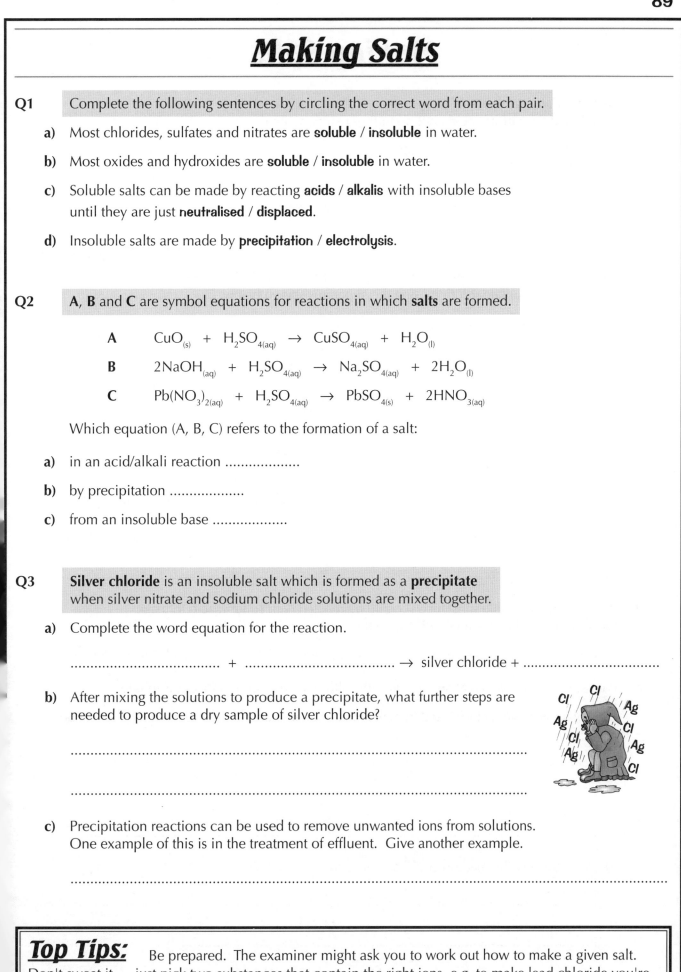

b) After mixing the solutions to produce a precipitate, what further steps are needed to produce a dry sample of silver chloride?

....

....

c) Precipitation reactions can be used to remove unwanted ions from solutions. One example of this is in the treatment of effluent. Give another example.

....

Top Tips: Be prepared. The examiner might ask you to work out how to make a given salt. Don't sweat it — just pick two substances that contain the right ions, e.g. to make lead chloride you're going to need lead ions and chloride ions. So far so good, but don't forget that the method you use depends on whether the salt you're making is soluble or insoluble... so like I say, be prepared.

Making Salts

Q4 **Nickel sulfate** (a soluble salt) can be made by adding an excess of insoluble **nickel oxide** to **sulfuric acid** until no further reaction occurs.

a) Give an observation that would show you that the reaction is complete.

....

....

acid

excess of nickel oxide

Once the reaction is complete, the excess nickel oxide can be separated from the nickel sulfate solution using the apparatus shown below.

b) i) Label the diagram which shows the separation process.

....

ii) What is this method of separation called?

....

....

....

c) Describe how you could produce solid crystals of nickel sulfate from nickel sulfate solution.

....

....

d) Which other insoluble substance(s) could be reacted with sulfuric acid to make **nickel sulfate** using this method? Circle the correct answer(s) below.

nickel   lead chloride   ammonium sulfate   nickel hydroxide

e) Potassium hydroxide, an **alkali**, reacts with sulfuric acid to form **potassium sulfate**.

i) Explain why the method used to make nickel sulfate needs to be modified for this reaction.

....

....

....

ii) Describe how the method could be changed.

....

....

....

Electrolysis

Q1 Fill in the blanks in the passage below using the words provided.

| electric current | liquid | conduct | atoms | electrolysis | molecules |
| flow | positive | elements | negative | ionic | free ions | molten |

If you pass an .... through an ....

substance that's .... or in solution, it breaks down into the

.... it's made of. This is called ....

It requires a .... to conduct the electricity, called the electrolyte.

Electrolytes contain .... which ....

the electricity. For an electrical circuit to be complete, there's got to be a

.... of electrons. Electrons are taken away from ions at the

.... electrode and given to other ions at the

.... electrode. As ions gain or lose electrons they become

.... or .... and are released.

Q2 **Lead bromide** is an ionic substance. It doesn't easily dissolve in water.

a) How could lead bromide be made into a liquid for electrolysis?

....

b) Give the **products** of the electrolysis of lead bromide.

....

c) Tick the correct boxes to show whether the following statements about the electrolysis of **lead bromide** are **true** or **false**.

True False

i) The bromide ions are oxidised. ☐ ☐

ii) Bromide ions are attracted to the negative electrode. ☐ ☐

iii) At the negative electrode, positively charged ions gain electrons. ☐ ☐

iv) Lead atoms become lead ions at the negative electrode. ☐ ☐

v) Oxidation is a gain of electrons. ☐ ☐

Top Tips: You probably tend to think of oxidation and reduction as gain or loss of oxygen. That's not wrong, but it's not always true either — it can refer to electrons being lost or gained.

Chemistry 2b — Reaction Rates, Salts and Electrolysis

Electrolysis of Sodium Chloride Solution

Q1   The table shows the products at the negative electrode when different solutions of **ionic substances** are electrolysed.

a)   What do you notice about the product released at the negative electrode and its position in the reactivity series?

....

....

....

Ionic Substance in Solution	Product at Negative Electrode
sodium nitrate	hydrogen
copper sulfate	copper
zinc iodide	hydrogen
potassium chloride	hydrogen
silver nitrate	silver

reactivity ↑

potassium
sodium
calcium
carbon
zinc
iron
lead
hydrogen
copper
silver

b)   A solution of iron chloride is electrolysed. What product would form at the negative electrode?

....

Q2   Use the words below to complete the passage about the electrolysis of **sodium chloride solution**.

chlorine   soap   sodium chloride   sodium hydroxide   plastics   bleach   negative electrode

During the electrolysis, ... is split into three useful products.

At the positive electrode .... gas is produced. This can be used in

the manufacture of .... and ....

At the .... hydrogen gas is given off. ....

is left in solution. This strong alkali is used to make ....

Q3   The diagram below shows the electrolysis of a **salt solution**.

a)   Identify the ions and molecules labelled A, B, C and D on the diagram. Choose from the options in the box below.

Na^+ H^+ Cl_2 H_2 Cl^- Na_2 H_2O

A ....   B ....

C ....   D ....

Negative Electrode (-ve)   Positive Electrode (+ve)

C   D
A   B

NaCl Solution

b)   Write **balanced** half-equations for the processes that occur at the electrodes during the electrolysis of this salt solution.

Positive electrode: ....

Negative electrode: ....

Make sure the charges balance.

Extraction of Aluminium and Electroplating

Q1 **Aluminium** is the most **abundant** metal in the Earth's crust.

Goodness, how awfully common... °°°°

a) **i)** Circle the correct word:

The most common aluminium ore is **bauxite / cryolite.**

ii) When this ore is mined and purified, which compound is obtained? Give its name and formula.

Name .... Formula ....

b) Tick the boxes to show whether the following statements are **true** or **false**.

	True	False
i) In the extraction of aluminium the electrolyte is molten aluminium metal.	☐	☐
ii) Aluminium oxide is dissolved in molten cryolite before electrolysis begins.	☐	☐
iii) Cryolite is used in the electrolysis of aluminium to keep the cost down.	☐	☐
iv) Copper electrodes are used in the extraction of aluminium by electrolysis.	☐	☐
v) Aluminium is formed at the positive electrode.	☐	☐

c) The positive electrode needs to be **replaced** frequently. Explain why.

....

....

Q2 Electroplating could be used to put a thin coat of **silver** onto a **nickel** fork.

a) Complete the diagram below by labelling the **negative electrode** and **positive electrode**.

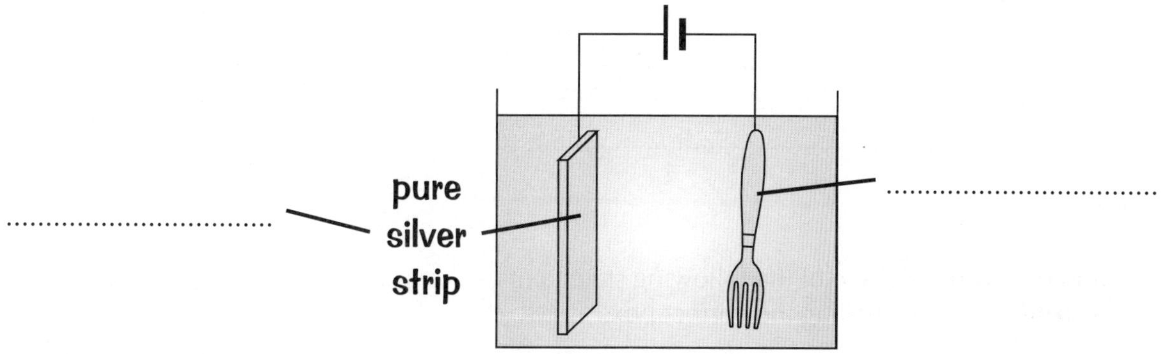

....

pure
silver
strip

....

b) What **ion** must the electrolyte contain?

....

c) Give **one** reason why you might want to electroplate a nickel fork with silver.

....

d) Give **one** other use of electroplating.

....

Mixed Questions — Chemistry 2b

Q1 Several factors affect **how quickly** chemical reactions occur.

a) Name four things that can **increase** the rate of a reaction.

1. .... 2. ....

3. .... 4. ....

b) Measuring the **amount of reactant used up** over time is one way to work out the rate of a reaction. Give the other thing that can be measured over time to give the rate of a reaction.

....

Q2 The graph shows the results from an experiment using magnesium and dilute hydrochloric acid. The **change in mass** of the reactants was measured using a balance.

a) Which reaction was **faster**, P or Q?

....

b) Which reaction used the **most** reactants, P, Q or R?

....

c) The reaction produces a **gas**. Which other experimental method could you have used to measure the rate of reaction?

....

....

Q3 Indicate whether each of the following statements is **true** or **false** by ticking the correct box.

True False

a) When measuring the change in mass of a reaction, the quicker the reading on the balance drops, the faster the reaction. ☐ ☐

b) Using a gas syringe to measure the volume of gas given off is usually quite accurate. ☐ ☐

c) An explosion is an example of a slow reaction. ☐ ☐

d) On a rate of reaction graph the line with the steepest slope shows the fastest rate of reaction. ☐ ☐

e) If the same amount of reactants are used the same amount of product will be produced, regardless of the rate of reaction. ☐ ☐

Mixed Questions — Chemistry 2b

Q4 The diagram shows the **pH scale**.

| 1 | 2 | 3 | 4 | 5 | 6 | 7 | 8 | 9 | 10 | 11 | 12 | 13 |

↑ black coffee   ↑ milk of magnesia

a) The pH values of black coffee and milk of magnesia are marked on the diagram.

   i) Is black coffee neutral, acidic or alkaline? ....

   ii) Is milk of magnesia neutral, acidic or alkaline? ....

b) **i)** Some milk of magnesia is added to some black coffee.
A reaction takes place. Name the type of reaction.

     ....

   ii) Would you expect this reaction to be exothermic or endothermic?

     ....

Q5 Rose added a piece of **magnesium** to some **HCl** and watched what happened.

a) Complete and **balance** the chemical equation for the reaction.

Mg + ... HCl → .... + ...

b) Explain how the **pH** would change as the magnesium was added.

....

c) What is the name of the salt formed from magnesium and **sulfuric acid**?

....

Q6 Aluminium is extracted from its ore by **electrolysis**.

a) The aluminium ions are attracted to the **negative** electrode.

   i) Explain what happens to the aluminium ions at the negative electrode.

     ....

     ....

   ii) Complete and balance the half-equation for this reaction. Include state symbols.

     $Al^{3+}_{(aq)}$ + ... → ....

b) The **oxygen** ions are attracted to the **positive** electrode. Complete and balance the half-equation for the reaction at the positive electrode. Include state symbols.

     $2O^{2-}_{(aq)}$ → .... + ...

Mixed Questions — Chemistry 2b

Q7 Explain why **cryolite** is used in the electrolysis of aluminium oxide.

....

....

Q8 Some solid **magnesium oxide** was added to **HCl** solution in a test tube. The reactants and the products are shown below, but the equation is **not** balanced. **D** is a mystery product.

$$MgO_{(s)} \quad + \quad HCl_{(aq)} \quad \rightarrow \quad D_{(aq)} \quad + \quad H_2O_{(l)}$$

a) **i)** Give the chemical formula of substance **D**. ....

ii) Write out a full balanced equation for the above reaction.

....

b) When solid magnesium oxide was added to a substance, **S**, magnesium sulfate and water were formed. Identify S by name or formula.

....

c) State whether metal oxides are **acids** or **bases**. ....

Q9 The electrolysis of **sodium chloride solution** gives useful products that can be used in industry.

a) **i)** Name the two products that form at the **electrodes**.

1. ....

2. ....

ii) Name an industrial use for one of these products.

....

b) When electrolysis is complete, **sodium hydroxide** (NaOH) remains in solution. Explain why this happens. Refer to reactivity in your answer.

....

....

....

c) Electrolysis is also used for electroplating. What is electroplating?

....

Chemistry 2b — Reaction Rates, Salts and Electrolysis

Velocity and Distance-Time Graphs

Q1 The **monorail** at Buffers' Theme Park takes people from the visitor centre to the main park and back again. It travels at the same **speed** on the outward and return journeys.

The monorail's velocity on the outward journey is 12 m/s. What is its velocity on the return journey?

....

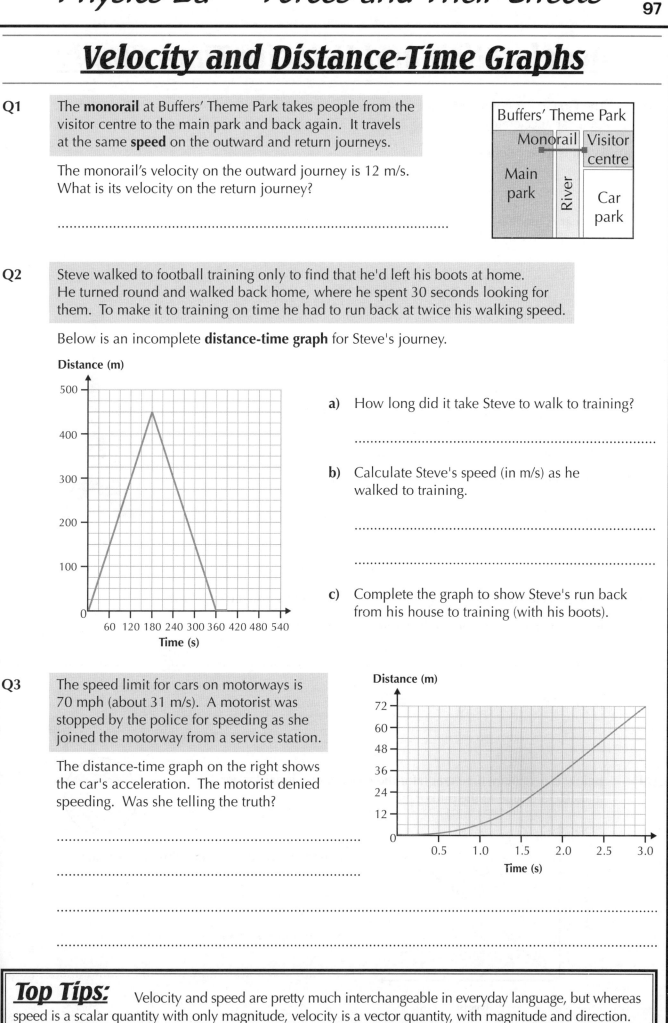

Buffers' Theme Park
Monorail | Visitor centre
Main park | River | Car park

Q2 Steve walked to football training only to find that he'd left his boots at home. He turned round and walked back home, where he spent 30 seconds looking for them. To make it to training on time he had to run back at twice his walking speed.

Below is an incomplete **distance-time graph** for Steve's journey.

Distance (m)

a) How long did it take Steve to walk to training?

....

b) Calculate Steve's speed (in m/s) as he walked to training.

....

....

c) Complete the graph to show Steve's run back from his house to training (with his boots).

Q3 The speed limit for cars on motorways is 70 mph (about 31 m/s). A motorist was stopped by the police for speeding as she joined the motorway from a service station.

The distance-time graph on the right shows the car's acceleration. The motorist denied speeding. Was she telling the truth?

....

....

....

....

Distance (m)

Top Tips: Velocity and speed are pretty much interchangeable in everyday language, but whereas speed is a scalar quantity with only magnitude, velocity is a vector quantity, with magnitude and direction.

Acceleration and Velocity-Time Graphs

Q1   The Go Go car company make gas-powered model cars.
One car accelerates from rest to 20 m/s in 3.5 s.

a)   What is its acceleration?

....

b)   The car is modified and now accelerates from 3 m/s to 20 m/s in 2.8 s.
Show that this modification has improved the car's acceleration.

....

....

Q2   An egg is dropped from the top of the Eiffel tower.
It hits the ground after 8 seconds, at a speed of 80 m/s.

a)   Find the egg's acceleration. ....

b)   How long did it take for the egg to reach 40 m/s?

....

Q3   A car accelerates at 2 m/s². After 4 seconds it reaches a speed of 24 m/s.

How fast was it going before it started to accelerate?

....

....

Q4   Below is a velocity-time graph for the descent of a lunar lander.
It accelerates due to the pull of gravity from the Moon.

Use the graph to calculate this acceleration.

....

....

....

Physics 2a — Forces and Their Effects

Acceleration and Velocity-Time Graphs

Q5 Describe the **type of motion** happening at each of the labelled points on the velocity-time graph.

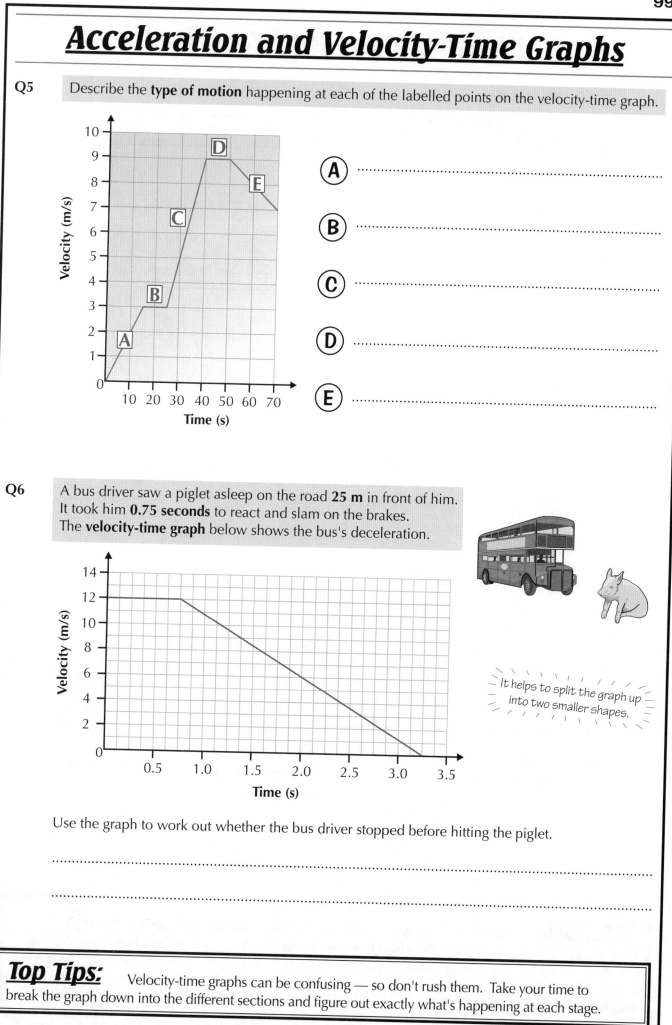

(A) ....

(B) ....

(C) ....

(D) ....

(E) ....

Q6 A bus driver saw a piglet asleep on the road **25 m** in front of him.
It took him **0.75 seconds** to react and slam on the brakes.
The **velocity-time graph** below shows the bus's deceleration.

It helps to split the graph up into two smaller shapes.

Use the graph to work out whether the bus driver stopped before hitting the piglet.

....

....

Top Tips: Velocity-time graphs can be confusing — so don't rush them. Take your time to break the graph down into the different sections and figure out exactly what's happening at each stage.

Weight, Mass and Gravity

Q1 Fill in the gaps in the following paragraph using the words below:

kilograms	newtons	mass	weight	gravitational

The .... of an object is just the amount of 'stuff' it's made up of. It doesn't

change, regardless of where in the universe it is, and it's measured in ....

.... is a force and is measured in .... — it's the

.... force that one object (e.g. a planet) exerts on another (e.g. an apple).

Q2 Joni has been feeding her dog Fluffy a bit too much bacon. The vet decides he needs to go on a diet.

g = 10 N/kg

a) Joni puts Fluffy on some scales and finds he has a mass of **58 kg**. Calculate his **weight**.

....

b) After three weeks of Fluffy eating only 'Skinny Dog' biscuits, Joni weighs Fluffy by putting him in a sling and hanging him from a **newton meter**. He now has a weight of **460 N**. How much **mass** has he lost?

....

....

Q3 An astronaut goes to Mars to do some experiments.

a) Explain why her **mass** stays the same but her **weight** changes.

Woohoo!
Who needs diets?
Just go to Mars...

....

....

b) She takes a rock that weighs **50 N** on Earth. Using a set of scales designed for use on Earth, she finds that the mass of the rock appears to be **1.9 kg** on Mars. Calculate the **gravitational field strength** on Mars.

....

....

Top Tips: Gravity may be keeping you down to the earth, but compared to the other fundamental forces, it is actually **surprisingly weak**. Think about it — you have whole Earth pulling you downwards but you can jump and hop and skip away from it without too much effort. Then think about how much effort it can take to pull opposite ends of a small magnet apart. The fact is, **anything that has mass has gravity**, but objects have to be pretty humongous before anyone notices.

Physics 2a — Forces and Their Effects

Resultant Forces

Q1   A teapot sits on a table.

a)   Explain why it doesn't sink into the table.

....

b)   Chris carelessly knocks the teapot off the table and it accelerates towards the floor.

i)   Explain whether the vertical forces are balanced.

....

ii)   The teapot hits the floor without breaking and bounces upwards.
Name the force that causes the teapot to bounce upwards.

....

Q2   A bear rides a bike north at a constant speed.

a)   Label the forces acting on the bear.

....

b)   The bear brakes and slows down.
Are the forces balanced **as** he
slows down? If not, which
direction is the resultant force in?

....

....

....

Q3   The **force diagram** on the right shows a **train** pulling out of a station.

Calculate the resultant force acting on
the train in the following directions:

1 500 000 N

6 000 000 N

1 500 000 N

a)   Vertical: ....

b)   Horizontal: ....

1 500 000 N

Q4   State whether there is a resultant force in each of the following situations. Explain your answers.

a)   A cricket ball slowing down as it rolls along the outfield.

....

b)   A car going round a roundabout at a steady 30 mph.

....

c)   A vase sat on a window ledge.

....

Forces and Acceleration

Q1 Use the words supplied to fill in the blanks in the paragraph below.

| interact | resultant force | stationary | accelerates |
| opposite | constant | non-zero | balanced |

If the forces on an object are .... , it's either ....

or moving at .... speed. If an object has a ....

resultant force acting on it, it .... in the direction of the

.... When two objects .... ,

the forces they exert on each other are equal and ....

Q2 You're travelling home from school on a bus doing a steady speed in a straight line. Which of the following is true? Tick the appropriate box.

☐ The driving force of the engine is bigger than friction and air resistance combined.

☐ There are no forces acting on the bus.

☐ The driving force of the engine is equal to friction and air resistance combined.

☐ A resultant force is required to keep the bus moving.

Q3 The diagram below shows the **forces** acting on an aeroplane.

lift, thrust, air resistance, weight

a) The aircraft is flying horizontally at a constant speed of 200 m/s. Which of the following statements about the aeroplane is true? Circle the appropriate letter.

A The thrust is bigger than the air resistance and the lift is bigger than the weight.

B The thrust is smaller than the air resistance and the lift is equal to the weight.

C The thrust is equal to the air resistance and the lift is equal to the weight.

D The thrust is equal to the air resistance and the lift is bigger than the weight.

b) What happens to the forces as the plane descends for landing and slows down to 100 m/s? Choose the correct options to complete the following statements:

i) The thrust is **greater than / less than / equal to** the air resistance.

ii) The lift is **greater than / less than / equal to** the weight.

Remember — the plane is losing height as well as slowing down.

Stopilithea削.

Forces and Acceleration

Q4 Put these cars in order of increasing driving force.

Car	Mass (kg)	Maximum acceleration (m/s²)
Disraeli 9000	800	5
Palmerston 6i	1560	0.7
Heath TT	950	3
Asquith 380	790	2

1. ....
2. ....
3. ....
4. ....

Q5 Jo and Brian have fitted both their scooters with the same engine. Brian and his scooter have a combined mass of 110 kg and an acceleration of 2.80 m/s². On her scooter, Jo only manages an acceleration of 1.71 m/s².

a) What **force** can the engine exert?

....

b) Calculate the combined mass of Jo and her scooter.

....

Q6 Tom drags a 1 kg mass along a table with a newton-meter so that it accelerates at 0.25 m/s². If the newton-meter reads 0.4 N, what's the force of friction between the mass and the table?

....

....

....

Q7 A car tows a caravan along a road. At a constant speed, the pulling force of the car and the opposing reaction force of the caravan are equal. Which statement correctly describes the forces between the caravan and the car when the car accelerates? Tick the appropriate box.

☐ "The caravan's reaction force cancels out the pulling force of the car, so the caravan won't accelerate."

☐ "The caravan's reaction force is at a right angle to the force pulling the car, so the two forces don't affect one another."

☐ "The car's pulling force accelerates the caravan. The caravan's reaction acts on the car, not the caravan."

Forces and Acceleration

Q8 Which of the following statements correctly explains what happens when you walk?
Tick the appropriate box.

☐ Your feet push backwards on the ground, so the ground pushes you forwards.

☐ The force in your muscles overcomes the friction between your feet and the ground.

☐ The ground's reaction can't push you backwards because of friction.

☐ Your feet push forwards, and the ground's reaction is upwards.

Q9 A camper van with a mass of 2500 kg has a maximum driving force of 2650 N.
It is driven along a straight, level road at a constant speed of 90 kilometres per hour.
At this speed, air resistance is 2000 N and the friction between the wheel bearings is 500 N.

a) **i)** What force is the engine exerting? ....

ii) Complete the diagram to show all the forces acting on the camper van.
Give the size of each force.

b) A strong headwind begins blowing, with a force of **200 N**. The van slows down.
Calculate its deceleration.

....

c) The driver notices that the van is slowing and puts his foot right down on the accelerator,
applying the maximum driving force. How does the acceleration of the camper van change?
(Assume that air resistance and friction remain at their previous values.)

....

....

....

Top Tips: A resultant force means your object will accelerate — it will change its speed
or direction (or both). But if your object has a constant speed (which could be zero) and a constant
direction, you can say with utter confidence that there ain't any resultant force. Be careful though
— a zero resultant force doesn't mean there are **no** forces, just that they all balance each other out.

Frictional Force and Terminal Velocity

Q1 Use the words supplied to fill in the blanks in the paragraph below about a skydiver. You may need to use some words more than once, or not at all.

decelerates   decrease   less   balances   increase   constant   greater   accelerates

When a skydiver jumps out of a plane, his weight is .... than his air resistance, so he .... downwards. This causes his air resistance to .... until it .... his weight. At this point, his velocity is .... When his parachute opens, his air resistance is .... than his weight, so he ....

This causes his air resistance to .... until it .... his weight. Then his velocity is .... once again.

Q2 Which of the following will **reduce** the air resistance force on an aeroplane? Tick any appropriate boxes.

☐ **flying higher (where the air is thinner)**   ☐ **carrying less cargo**

☐ **flying more slowly**   ☐ **making the plane more streamlined**

Q3 A scientist plans to investigate gravity by dropping a hammer and a feather from a tall building. Two onlookers predict what will happen. Say whether each is right or wrong, and explain why.

Paola: "They will land at the same time — gravity is the same for both."

Guiseppe: "The feather will reach its terminal velocity before the hammer."

a) Paola is **right** / **wrong** because ....

....

b) Guiseppe is **right** / **wrong** because ....

....

Q4 Mavis is investigating **drag** by dropping balls into a measuring cylinder full of oil and timing how long they take to reach the bottom. She does the experiment with a **golf ball**, a **glass marble** and a **ball bearing**.

From this experiment, can Mavis draw any conclusions about the effect of size on drag? Explain your answer.

....

....

Frictional Force and Terminal Velocity

Q5 The graph shows how the velocity of a skydiver changes before and after he opens his parachute.

For each of the four regions A-D tick the correct box to say whether the force of **weight** or **air resistance** is greater, or if they are **equal**.

	weight is greater	air resistance is greater	both equal
Region A:	☐	☐	☐
Region B:	☐	☐	☐
Region C:	☐	☐	☐
Region D:	☐	☐	☐

Q6 Two skydivers jump out of a plane. Kate opens her parachute after three seconds, when she is still accelerating rapidly. Alison doesn't open her parachute yet but uses her video camera to film Kate's skydive. On the film Kate's parachute appears to pull her suddenly upwards when it opens.

a) Is Kate really moving upwards? Explain your answer. ....

....

b) Describe how Kate's velocity changes when her parachute opens. ....

....

Q7 On **Venus**, atmospheric pressure is about 90 times that on Earth, but the gravitational field strength is about the same.
On **Mars**, atmospheric pressure is about 1/100th of that on Earth and the gravitational field strength is less than half that on Earth.

Higher atmospheric pressure means the atmosphere is <u>thicker</u> and provides <u>more resistance</u>.

Probes which land on other planets often need parachutes to slow them down during their descent. What **size** of parachute would you recommend, relative to a parachute used on Earth, for:

a) landing on Venus: ....

b) landing on Mars: ....

Top Tips: When objects move through the air at high speed, the air resistance is proportional to the object's **velocity squared**. That's why, for skydivers, air resistance soon balances their weight and they reach terminal velocity. It's also why **driving** very fast is very **inefficient**.

Physics 2a — Forces and Their Effects

Stopping Distances

Q1   **Stopping distance** and **braking distance** are not the same thing.

a)   What is meant by 'braking distance'?

....

b)   What is meant by 'thinking distance'?

....

Q2   Will the following factors affect **thinking** distance, **braking** distance or **both**?
Write them in the relevant columns of the table.

tiredness   road surface   weather   speed   drugs
alcohol   tyres   brakes   load

Thinking Distance	Braking Distance

Q3   A car joins a motorway and changes speed from 30 mph to 60 mph.
Which of the following statements are **true**? Tick the appropriate boxes.

☐   The total stopping distance will increase.

☐   The braking force needed to stop in a certain distance will decrease.

☐   Thinking distance will decrease.

☐   Both thinking and braking distance will increase.

Q4   A car has just driven through a deep puddle, making the brakes wet.
Explain why this will increase the stopping distance of the car.

....

....

Q5   Sam is driving when she receives a text message. She decides to try and read it
while still driving. Does this affect her thinking distance? Explain your answer.

....

....

Work and Potential Energy

Q1 Jenny kicks a football, giving it **50 J** of energy.

   a) How much work does Jenny do?

....

   b) If Jenny kicks the ball with a force of **250 N**, over what **distance** does her kick act on the ball?

....

Q2 Explain why pushing your bicycle along a **level** road means that you do some **work** in the scientific sense.

....

....

Q3 Indicate whether the following statements are **true** or **false**.

	True	False
a) Gravitational potential energy = mass × g × height.	☺	☹
b) Work done is the energy possessed by an object due to height.	☺	☹
c) On Earth, the gravitational field strength is approximately **10 N/kg**.	☺	☹
d) When a force moves an object, work is done.	☺	☹
e) On Earth, a **3 kg** chicken flies up 2.5 m to sit on a fence. It gains **90 J** of gravitational potential energy.	☺	☹

Q4 Dave works at a DIY shop. He has to load **28** flagstones onto the delivery truck. Each flagstone has a mass of **25 kg** and has to be lifted **1.2 m** onto the truck.

   a) How much gravitational potential energy does one flagstone gain when lifted onto the truck?

....

   b) What is the **total gravitational potential energy** gained by the flagstones after they are all loaded onto the truck?

....

   c) How much **work** does Dave do loading the truck?

....

....

Top Tips: The main thing to remember is that **energy transferred** and **work done** are just the **same** thing. You're bound to get asked to do a calculation, so make sure you know the couple of equations and how to use them. All work questions are pretty similar — so just keep practising and you'll be fine.

Work and Potential Energy

Q5 Shelagh keeps fit by cycling every day. She's calculated that she applies a steady force of **50 N** as she cycles. She decides to do at least **80 kJ** of work at each session.

a) What is the minimum distance Shelagh needs to cycle each session?

....

b) i) Shelagh unexpectedly comes to a large hill. She does **90 kJ** of work to climb a vertical height of **120 m**. Calculate the size of the force she does work against. Name this force.

....

....

ii) Calculate the combined mass of Shelagh and her bike.

....

Q6 Jo is sitting at the top of a helter-skelter ride and her mass is **50 kg**.

a) If her gravitational potential energy is **4000 J**, how high up is Jo?

....

b) She comes down the helter-skelter and at the bottom her kinetic energy is **1500 J**. How much **energy** has been 'wasted' coming down the ride?

....

c) Which **force** causes this energy to be wasted? ....

d) If the ride is **50 m** long, what is the average energy-wasting force?

....

e) Jo has another go on the helter-skelter but this time she slides down on a mat. At the bottom of the ride, her kinetic energy is **2000 J**. What is the average energy-wasting **force** on this turn on the ride?

....

....

f) Explain why Jo has a **different** kinetic energy at the bottom when she slides down on a mat.

....

g) At the bottom of the ride Jo and the mat take a distance of **5 m** to stop. What is the average stopping **force**?

....

....

Kinetic Energy

Q1 Decide if the following statements are **true** or **false**.

  True False

a) Kinetic energy is energy due to movement.

b) Heat from the Sun causes space shuttles to heat up as they re-enter the atmosphere.

c) Friction between meteors and the atmosphere causes most meteors to burn up before they reach the Earth.

Q2 A toy cricket ball hit straight upwards has a gravitational potential energy of **242 J** at the **top** of its flight.

a) What is the ball's **kinetic energy just** before it hits the ground?

....

b) Calculate the speed of the ball at this time if its mass is **100 g**.

....

Q3 A large truck and a car both have a kinetic energy of **614 400 J**. The mass of the truck is **12 288 kg** and the car **1200 kg**.

a) Calculate the **speed** of:

i) the car ....

ii) the truck ....

b) John is playing with his remote-controlled toy car and truck. The car's mass is 100 g. The truck's mass is 300 g. The car is moving twice as fast as the truck. Which has more kinetic energy — the car or the truck? Explain your answer.

....

....

Q4 Jack rides his bicycle along a level road and has a total kinetic energy of **1440 J**. He brakes, exerting a force of **200 N** on the wheels.

a) How far does he travel before he stops?

....

b) What happens to the temperature of the brakes? Explain your answer.

....

Top Tips: It's all about moving — the bigger the mass and the faster something moves the larger its kinetic energy. Get friendly with that formula — it crops up everywhere.

Forces and Elasticity

Q1   Alice is bouncing on a trampoline. Springs around the edge hold the trampoline bed in place.

a)   The springs that hold the trampoline bed are **elastic objects**. Describe what 'elastic' means.

....

b)   When she is at the top of a bounce
Alice has **gravitational potential energy**.
This is transferred to **kinetic energy** as
she falls back down, but at the bottom
of the bounce the kinetic energy is **zero**.
Explain what happens to her kinetic energy.

....

....

c)   Alice exerts a force of 600 N on the trampoline at the bottom of her bounce

i)   There are 30 springs that support the trampoline bed. Calculate the **force exerted per spring**.
Assume that **only the springs extend**, and that this force is **evenly spread** across the springs.

....

ii) An individual spring extends by **10 cm** at the bottom of a bounce. Calculate its **spring constant**.

....

....

Q2   Nick the bungee jumper is checking his bungee cords.

a)   One cord has a spring constant **45 N/m**. Calculate how much force is required to stretch it by **15 m**.

....

b)   Nick conducts an experiment to find how much force it takes to stretch the bungee rope by
different amounts. His results are plotted on the graph below and a best fit line is drawn.

i) Name the point labelled **P**.

....

ii) Nick repeats his experiment with the **same bungee cord**
and plots the results in a graph. Will he get an identical
force-extension curve? Explain your answer.

....

....

....

Power

Q1 Complete this passage by using the words provided.

heat	energy	one hundred	rate	light	watts	joules

Power is the .... of doing work, or how much .... is

transferred per second. It is measured in .... or ....

per second. A 100 W light bulb transfers .... joules of electrical

energy into .... and .... each second.

Q2 George drives to work every day in a small car with a **power** output of **50 kW**.

a) Write down an equation that relates **power** to **energy**.

....

b) If the journey takes **5 minutes**, how much **energy** does the car get from its fuel?

....

c) One day George's car breaks down and so he cycles to work. The journey takes him
12 minutes and he uses **144 kJ** of energy. How much **power** does he generate?

....

Q3 Catherine and Sally decide to run up a set of stairs to see who can get to the
top more quickly. Catherine has a mass of **46 kg** and Sally has a mass of **48 kg**. $g = 10 \text{ N/kg}$

a) The top of the stairs is **5 m** above ground.
Calculate the gain in **potential energy** for:

i) Catherine

....

ii) Sally

....

b) Catherine won the race in **6.2 s**, while Sally took **6.4 s**.
Which girl generated more **power**?

....

....

Power

Q4 Tom likes to build model boats. His favourite boat is the Carter, which has a motor power of **150 W**.

a) How much **energy** does the Carter transfer in **10 minutes**?

....

b) The petrol for the boat's motor can supply **30 kJ/ml**.
What volume of petrol is used up in **10 minutes**?

....

c) Tom decides to get a model speed boat which transfers **120 kJ** in the same 10 minute journey.
What is the **power** of the engine?

....

Q5 Josie runs home after school so she can watch her favourite TV programme.
She has a mass of **60 kg** and her school bag has a mass of **6 kg**.

a) At the start of her run, she accelerates steadily from **0** to **8 m/s** in **6 seconds** while carrying her bag.
Calculate her power for this part of her run.

....

b) Josie gets to her house, she puts **down** her school bag, and then runs up the stairs to her room.
It takes her **4 seconds** to get to the top of the stairs, where she is **5 m** above ground level.
How much power does she generate getting up the stairs?

....

Q6 Andy loves running and wants to improve his starts in sprint races. He uses a timing gate to measure his maximum speed and how long the start takes him. He has a mass of **70 kg**.

Sprint number	Time taken (s)	Maximum speed (m/s)
1	3.2	8.0
2	3.1	8.2
3	3.3	7.9
4 *	4.6	7.2
5	3.2	7.9

*He slips at the start because his shoes don't grip properly.

a) Andy records data for five starts as shown. Which start data set should be ignored?

....

b) Calculate the average **time** taken and the average **speed** achieved in the reliable starts.

....

....

c) What is Andy's average **power** over the reliable starts?

....

Momentum and Collisions

Q1   Circle the correct words or phrases to make the following statements true.

a)   If the velocity of a moving object doubles, its **kinetic energy** / **momentum** will double.

b)   If you drop a suitcase out of a moving car, the car's momentum will **decrease** / **increase**.

c)   When two objects collide the total momentum **changes** / **stays the same**.

d)   When a force acts on an object its momentum **changes** / **stays the same**.

Q2   Place the following four trucks in order of increasing momentum.

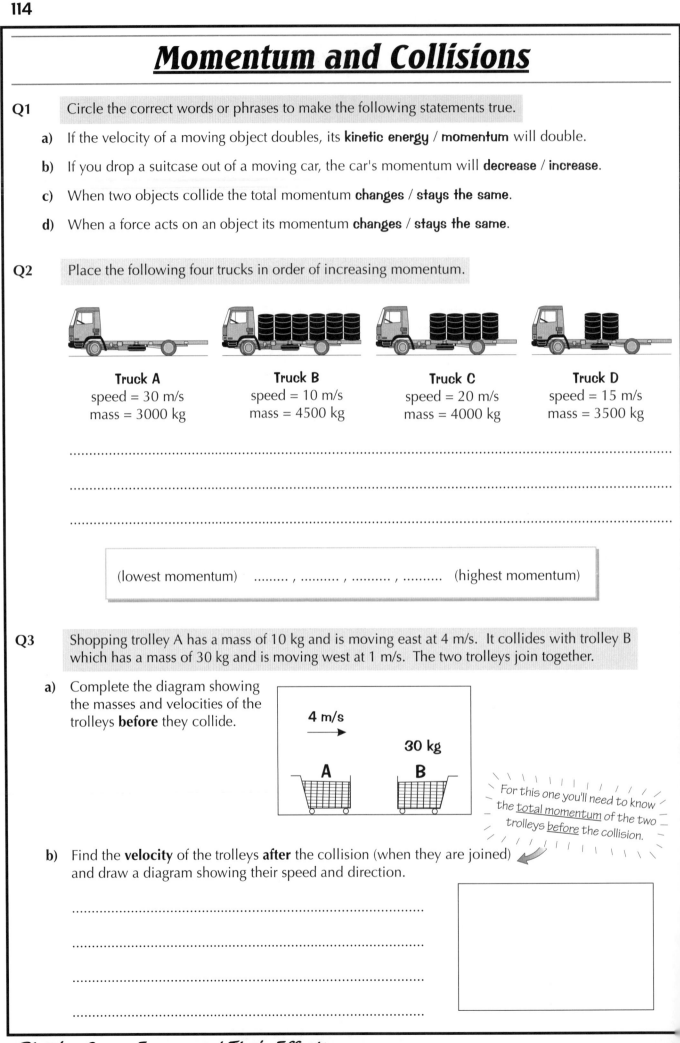

Truck A
speed = 30 m/s
mass = 3000 kg

Truck B
speed = 10 m/s
mass = 4500 kg

Truck C
speed = 20 m/s
mass = 4000 kg

Truck D
speed = 15 m/s
mass = 3500 kg

....

....

....

(lowest momentum)   .... , ... , ... , ...   (highest momentum)

Q3   Shopping trolley A has a mass of 10 kg and is moving east at 4 m/s. It collides with trolley B which has a mass of 30 kg and is moving west at 1 m/s. The two trolleys join together.

a)   Complete the diagram showing the masses and velocities of the trolleys **before** they collide.

4 m/s

30 kg

A   B

For this one you'll need to know the <u>total momentum</u> of the two trolleys <u>before</u> the collision.

b)   Find the **velocity** of the trolleys **after** the collision (when they are joined) and draw a diagram showing their speed and direction.

....

....

....

....

Physics 2a — Forces and Their Effects

Car Design and Safety

Q1   Use the words in the box to fill in the gaps in the paragraph below.

electric generator	reverse	heat	chemical
efficient		work	regenerative

When the brakes of a car are applied, they do .... on the

wheels, transferring kinetic energy into .... and sound

energy. New .... braking systems put the vehicle's motor

into .... to slow the wheels down.

The motor works as an .... and converts the kinetic

energy of the wheels into electrical energy. This can then be used to charge

the vehicle's battery — storing the electrical energy as ....

energy. By finding a use for this previously 'wasted' energy, these new braking

systems make cars more ....

Q2   A car travels along a level road and brakes to avoid hitting a cat.

a)   What type of **energy** does the moving car have?

....

b)   Explain how energy is **conserved** as the brakes slow down the car.

....

....

Q3   Clive's car has a top speed of 150 mph. He attaches a roof box to his car. How will this affect its top speed? Explain your answer.

....

....

....

Car Design and Safety

Q4   Modern cars are now fitted with many **safety features**, including seat belts.

a)   Explain why car safety features are designed to **slow** the car and
its occupants down over the **longest** possible time in a collision.

....

....

b)   State **two other** safety features which increase the time taken for passengers to slow down in a
crash. For each feature, explain **how** it helps to convert **kinetic energy** more safely.

....

....

....

....

Q5   Since 1991 it has been compulsory in the UK for all adults
to wear seat belts in both the front and back seats of a car.

a)   Explain how a seat belt **absorbs** energy to
slow down a passenger when a crash occurs.

....

b)   Explain, in terms of **momentum changes**, how this protects the passenger's internal organs.

....

....

....

Q6   A sports car transfers **2 650 000 kJ** of chemical energy
per hour into kinetic energy. Calculate its power output.

$power = energy \div time$

....

....

....

Top Tips: In a car crash there's a sudden change in velocity, which means a sudden change in
momentum. To help protect the passengers inside, the car needs to make the momentum change more
slowly — if you're in a serious crash you want the car to be the one all crumpled up, not you.

Physics 2a — Forces and Their Effects

Mixed Questions — Physics 2a

Q1 Mr Alonso drives his car at a constant speed for **1500 m**. The engine produces a force of **300 N**.

a) How much work does the engine do?

300 N ➡

....

b) Mr. Alonso then accelerates, increasing his speed by 20 m/s over 6.2 s. Calculate his acceleration.

....

c) As it's a hot day, Mr. Alonso winds down his windows.
Explain how and why this will alter the **top speed** of the car.

....

....

d) Explain how wearing a seat belt will keep Mr. Alonso safer in a crash.

....

....

e) Explain how the crumple zones of the car decrease the force on Mr. Alonso in a crash.

....

....

Q2 Jack and Jill go up a hill to go on a roller coaster. With them in it, the roller coaster carriage has a total mass of **1200 kg**.

a) What is the weight of the carriage? (Assume g = 10 N/kg.) ....

b) At the start of the ride the carriage rises up to its highest point of **34 m** above the ground and stops. Calculate its gain in gravitational potential energy.

....

c) The carriage then falls to a third of its maximum height. Assuming there is no air resistance or friction, calculate the speed of the carriage at this point.

....

....

....

d) At the end of the ride, the carriage slows down, decelerating at **6.4 m/s²**.
How long does it take the carriage to slow down from 20 m/s and come to a stop?

....

....

Mixed Questions — Physics 2a

Q3 Norman loves trainspotting. As a special treat, he not only notes the train numbers but plots a **distance-time** graph for two of the trains.

    a) For how long is train 2 stationary?

    ....

    b) Both trains start at a steady speed.
        How do we know this?

    ....

    c) Calculate the initial speed of the faster train.

    ....

    d) Describe the motion of train 1 between 40 s and 80 s.

    ....

Q4 Cherie and Tony rob a bank. They escape in a getaway car with a mass of **2100 kg** and travel at a constant speed of **90 km/h** along a straight, level road.

    a) Is there a resultant force on the car? Explain your answer.

    ....

    b) Calculate the momentum of the car.

    ....

    c) A police car swings into the middle of the road and stops ahead of Cherie's car.
        Cherie slams on the brakes. The car comes to a halt **3.0 s** after she hits the brakes.

       i) Write down **two** factors that could affect Cherie's thinking distance.

         1. ....

         2. ....

      ii) Assuming the car decelerates uniformly, find the force acting on the braking car.

        ....

        ....

        ....

Top Tips: These mixed questions are like a good quality pick 'n' mix — there's a bit of everything in there: velocity, force, work, momentum, mass... And that's just what the exam will be like.

Mixed Questions — Physics 2a

Q5   In the film 'Crouching Sparrow, Hidden Beaver', a **95 kg** dummy is
dropped **60 m** from the top of a building. (Assume that g = 10 m/s².)

a)   Sketch a distance-time graph and a velocity-time graph for the dummy
from the moment it is dropped until just after it hits the ground.
(Ignore air resistance and assume the dummy does not reach a terminal speed.)

b)   The take doesn't go to plan so the dummy is lifted back to the top of the building using a motor.

   i)   How much work is done on the dummy to get it to the top of the building?

   ....

   ii)   The useful power output of the motor is **760 W**.
How long does it take to get the dummy to the top of the building?

   ....

c)   The dummy is getting a bit damaged, being dropped repeatedly, so an elastic cord is attached to it.
Calculate the **spring constant** of the cord if it stretches by **5 m** when the dummy is hanging on the end.

....

Q6   A sky-diver jumps out of an aeroplane. Her weight is **700 N**.

a)   What force causes her to accelerate downwards?

....

b)   After **10 s** she is falling at a steady speed of **60 m/s**.
State the force of air resistance that is acting on her.

....

c)   She now opens her parachute, which increases the air resistance to **2000 N**.
Explain what happens immediately after she opens the parachute.

....

....

d)   After falling with her parachute open for **5 s**, the sky-diver is travelling at a steady speed of **4 m/s**.
What is the air resistance force now?

....

Static Electricity

Q1 **Circle** the pairs of charges that would attract each other and **underline** those that would repel.

positive and positive   positive and negative   negative and positive   negative and negative

Q2 Fill in the gaps in these sentences with the words below.

electrons	positive	static	friction	insulating	negative

.... electricity can build up when two .... materials
are rubbed together. The .... moves .... from one
material onto the other. This leaves a .... charge on one of the
materials and a .... charge on the other.

Q3 The sentences below are wrong. Write out a **correct** version for each.

a) A polythene rod becomes negatively charged when rubbed with a duster because it loses electrons.

....

....

b) When a negatively charged object and a positively charged object are brought together,
only the negative object exerts a force.

....

....

c) The closer two charged objects are together, the less strongly they attract or repel.

....

....

d) Electrical charges can't move very easily through metals.

....

....

Q4 Russell hates his jumper. Whenever he takes it off
his hair stands on end. Explain why this happens.

....

....

Current and Potential Difference

Q1 Use the words below to complete the passage.

reduces	voltage	decrease	charge	work

Electric current is the flow of electric .... around a circuit. Current flows

through a component which has a potential difference (.................................) across it.

The potential difference between two points in an circuit is the .... done per

coulomb of charge that passes between the points. Resistance .... the flow

of current — to increase the current in a circuit you can .... the resistance.

Q2 Connect the quantities with their units and their symbols.

A   V   Ω   Current   Resistance   Potential Difference   volts   amps   ohms

Q3 A 3 volt battery can supply a current of 5 amps for 20 minutes before it needs recharging.

a) Calculate how much charge the battery can provide before it needs recharging.

....

Tip: convert to seconds first.

....

b) Each coulomb of charge from the battery can carry 3 J of energy.
Calculate how much work the battery can do before it needs recharging.

....

Q4 Sally is comparing two lamps, A and B. She takes the measurements shown in the table.

Calculate the **missing values** and write them in the table.

	Lamp A	Lamp B
Current through lamp (A)	2	4
Potential difference across lamp (V)	3	2
Charge passing in 10 s (C)		
Work done in 10 s (J)		

Q5 The motor in a fan is attached to a 9 V battery.
If a current of 4 A flows through the motor for 7 minutes:

a) Calculate the total charge passed.

....

b) Calculate the work done by the motor.

....

Circuits — The Basics

Q1   Match up these items from a standard test circuit with the **correct description** and **symbol**.

ITEM	DESCRIPTION	SYMBOL
Cell	Provides the 'push' on the charge.	
Variable Resistor	The item you're testing.	
Component	Used to alter the current.	
Voltmeter	Measures the current.	
Ammeter	Measures the voltage.	

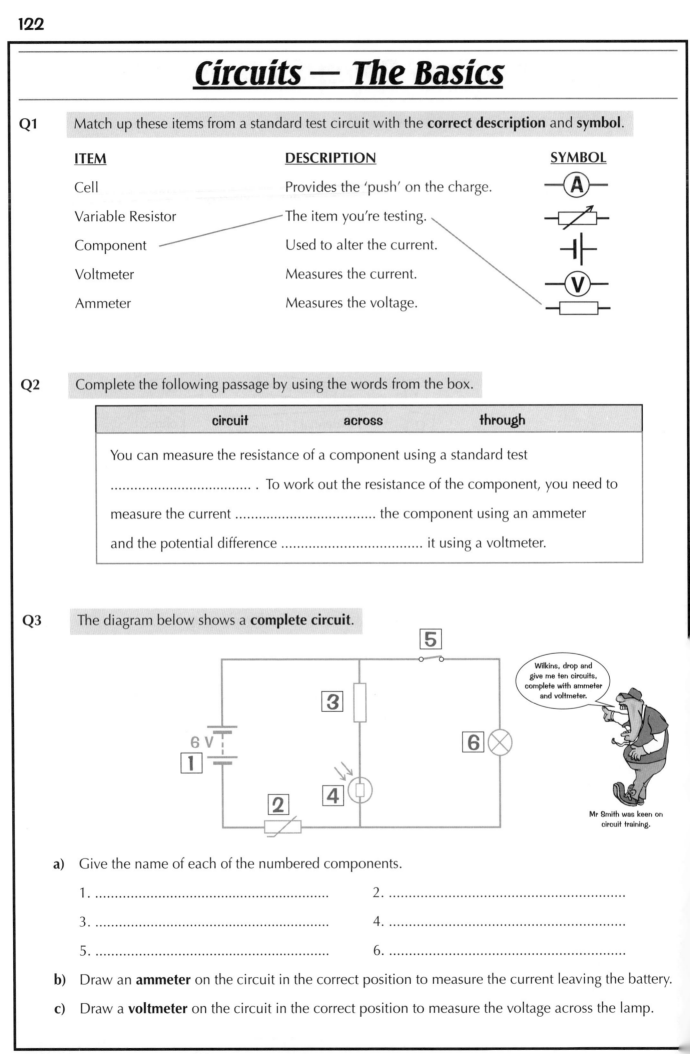

Q2   Complete the following passage by using the words from the box.

circuit	across	through

You can measure the resistance of a component using a standard test

.... To work out the resistance of the component, you need to

measure the current .... the component using an ammeter

and the potential difference .... it using a voltmeter.

Q3   The diagram below shows a **complete circuit**.

5

3

6 V   1

6

2

4

Wilkins, drop and give me ten circuits, complete with ammeter and voltmeter.

Mr Smith was keen on circuit training.

a)   Give the name of each of the numbered components.

1. ....   2. ....

3. ....   4. ....

5. ....   6. ....

b)   Draw an **ammeter** on the circuit in the correct position to measure the current leaving the battery.

c)   Draw a **voltmeter** on the circuit in the correct position to measure the voltage across the lamp.

Physics 2b — Electricity and the Atom

Resistance and V = I × R

Q1   Match the correct label to each of the **V-I graphs** below.

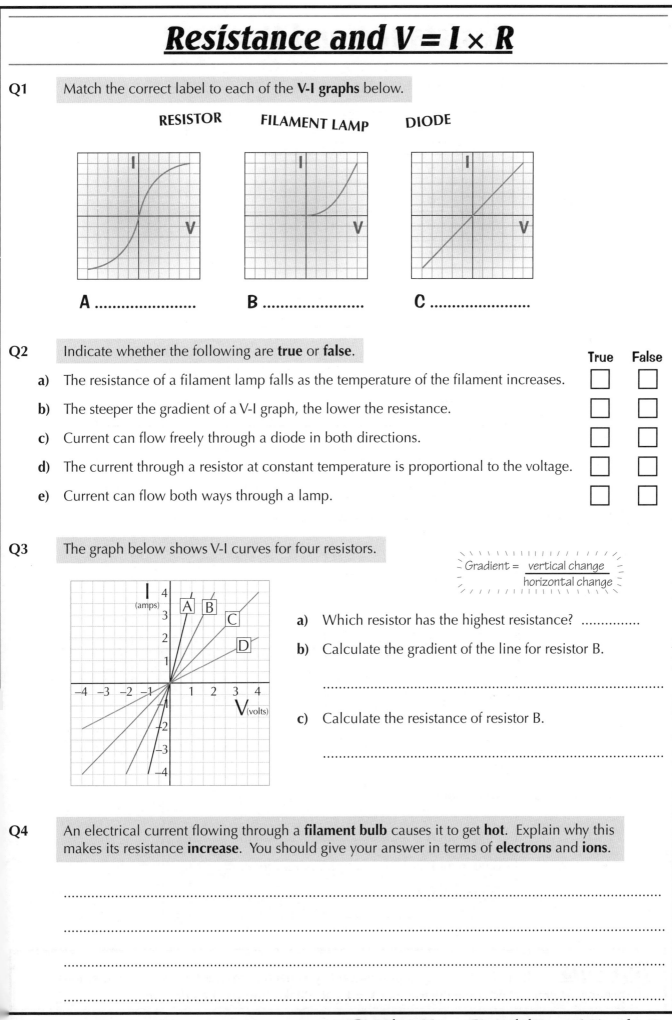

RESISTOR   FILAMENT LAMP   DIODE

A ....   B ....   C ....

Q2   Indicate whether the following are **true** or **false**.

		True	False
a)	The resistance of a filament lamp falls as the temperature of the filament increases.	☐	☐
b)	The steeper the gradient of a V-I graph, the lower the resistance.	☐	☐
c)	Current can flow freely through a diode in both directions.	☐	☐
d)	The current through a resistor at constant temperature is proportional to the voltage.	☐	☐
e)	Current can flow both ways through a lamp.	☐	☐

Q3   The graph below shows V-I curves for four resistors.

Gradient = $\dfrac{\text{vertical change}}{\text{horizontal change}}$

a)   Which resistor has the highest resistance? ....

b)   Calculate the gradient of the line for resistor B.

....

c)   Calculate the resistance of resistor B.

....

Q4   An electrical current flowing through a **filament bulb** causes it to get **hot**. Explain why this makes its resistance **increase**. You should give your answer in terms of **electrons** and **ions**.

....

....

....

....

Resistance and $V = I \times R$

Q5 Fill in the missing values in the table below.

Use the formula triangle to help.

Voltage (V)	Current (A)	Resistance (Ω)
6	2	
8		2
	3	3
4	8	
2		4
	0.5	2

Q6 Peter tested **three components** using a standard test circuit. The table below shows his results.

Voltage (V)	−4.0	−3.0	−2.0	−1.0	0.0	1.0	2.0	3.0	4.0
Component **A** current (A)	−2.0	−1.5	−1.0	−0.5	0.0	0.5	1.0	1.5	2.0
Component **B** current (A)	0.0	0.0	0.0	0.0	0.0	0.2	1.0	2.0	4.5
Component **C** current (A)	−4.0	−3.5	−3.0	−2.0	0.0	2.0	3.0	3.5	4.0

a) Draw a **V-I graph** for each component on the axes below.

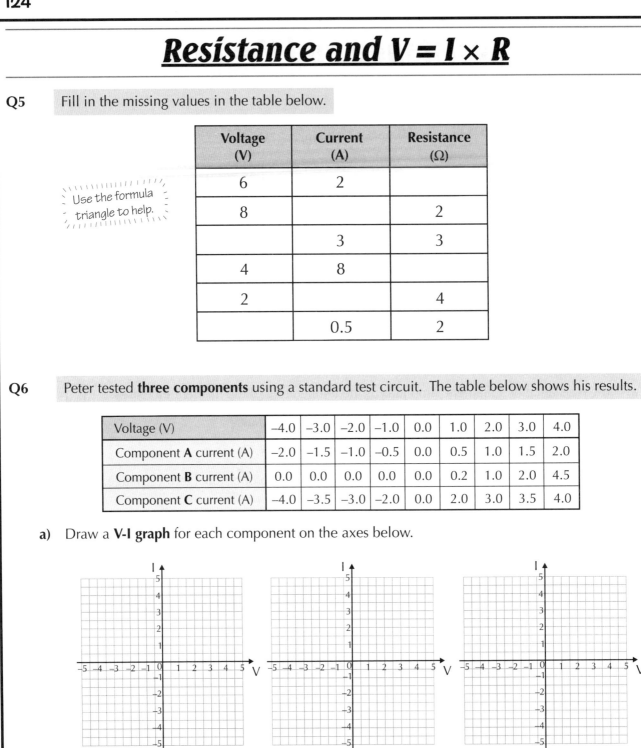

Component A   Component B   Component C

b) Complete Peter's **conclusions**:

Component **A** is a ....

Component **B** is a ....

Component **C** is a ....

Top Tips: There are two very important skills you need to master for resistance questions — **interpreting V-I graphs** and using the formula **V = I × R**. Make sure you can do both.

Circuit Devices

Q1   Use the words below to fill in the gaps. You won't need to use all the words.

light-dependent	lights	thermistor	vary	thermostats	diode

The resistance of some components can .... The resistance of a

.... goes up as the temperature decreases — this makes them useful as

electronic .... The resistance of a .... resistor

depends on the intensity of light falling on it — its resistance drops when light shines on it.

They're often used to automatically switch on .... when it gets dark.

Q2   **LEDs** are used in electrical appliances and for lighting.

a)   Briefly describe how an LED works.

....

b)   Suggest **one** reason why there is an increasing use of LEDs as lighting.

....

....

Q3   Look at the components below.

a)   Use **some** of the above components to design a circuit that will vary the brightness of a **lamp**, depending on the **temperature** in the room.

b)   What happens to the **resistance** in the circuit as the room temperature **increases**?

....

c)   What happens to the **brightness** of the lamp as the room temperature **decreases**?

....

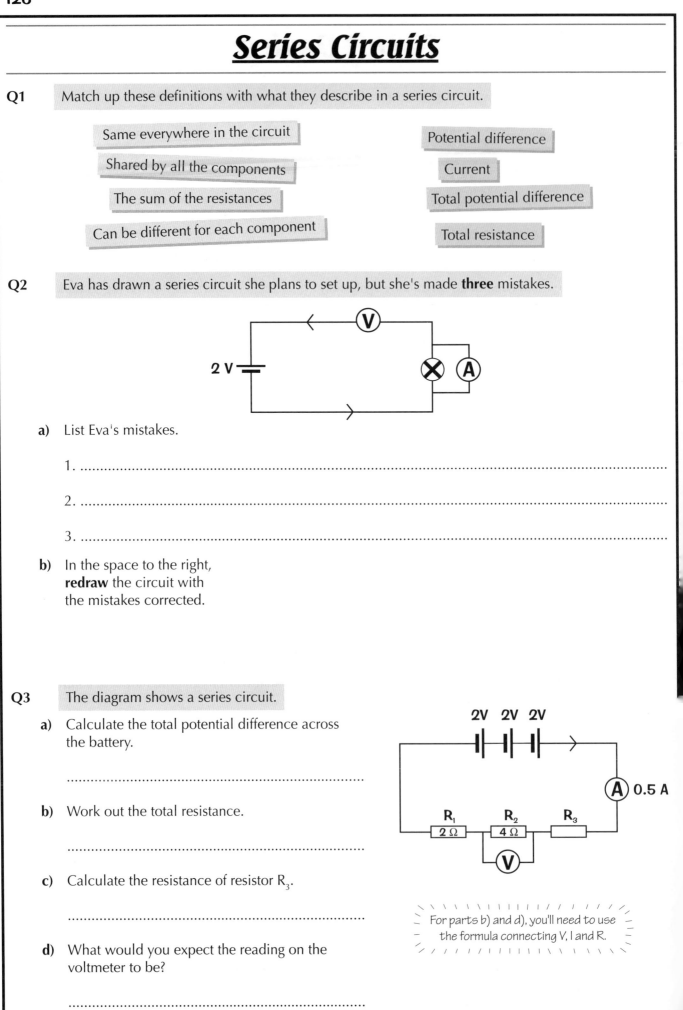

Series Circuits

Q1 Match up these definitions with what they describe in a series circuit.

Same everywhere in the circuit

Shared by all the components

The sum of the resistances

Can be different for each component

Potential difference

Current

Total potential difference

Total resistance

Q2 Eva has drawn a series circuit she plans to set up, but she's made **three** mistakes.

2 V

a) List Eva's mistakes.

1. ....

2. ....

3. ....

b) In the space to the right, **redraw** the circuit with the mistakes corrected.

Q3 The diagram shows a series circuit.

a) Calculate the total potential difference across the battery.

....

b) Work out the total resistance.

....

c) Calculate the resistance of resistor R₃.

....

d) What would you expect the reading on the voltmeter to be?

....

2V 2V 2V

(A) 0.5 A

R₁   R₂   R₃
2 Ω 4 Ω

(V)

For parts b) and d), you'll need to use the formula connecting V, I and R.

Physics 2b — Electricity and the Atom

Series Circuits

Q4 Vikram does an experiment with different numbers of lamps in a series circuit. The diagram below shows his three circuits.

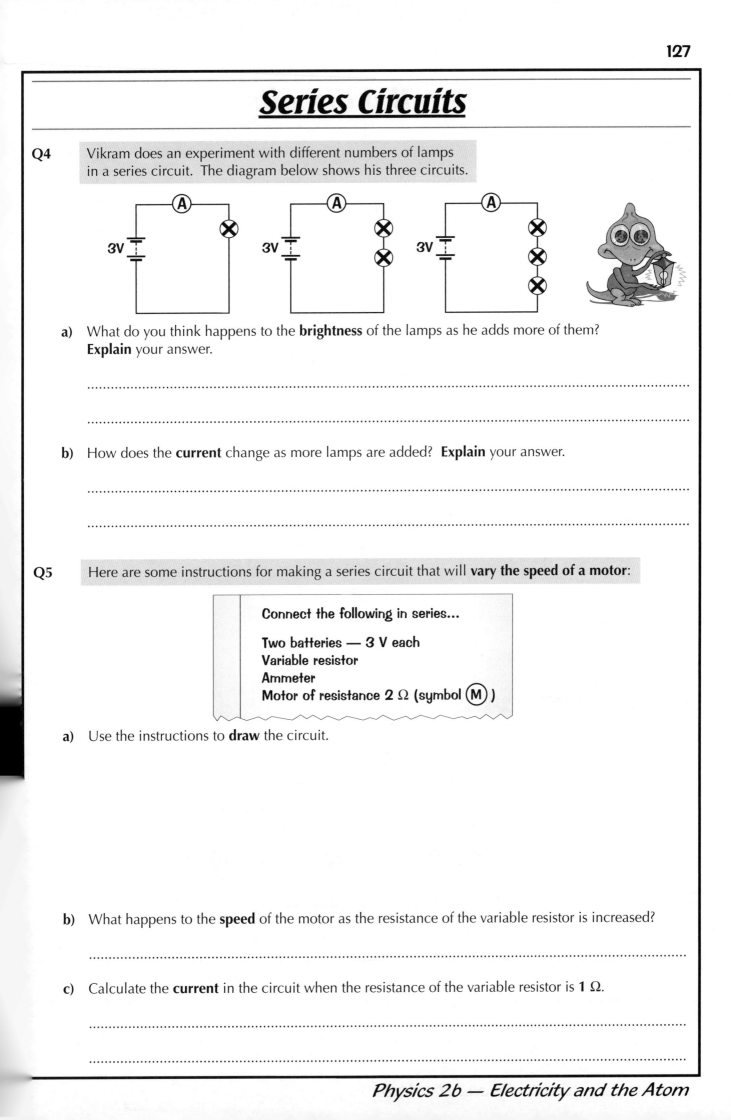

a) What do you think happens to the **brightness** of the lamps as he adds more of them? **Explain** your answer.

....

....

b) How does the **current** change as more lamps are added? **Explain** your answer.

....

....

Q5 Here are some instructions for making a series circuit that will **vary the speed of a motor**:

> **Connect the following in series...**
>
> Two batteries — 3 V each
> Variable resistor
> Ammeter
> Motor of resistance 2 Ω (symbol Ⓜ)

a) Use the instructions to **draw** the circuit.

b) What happens to the **speed** of the motor as the resistance of the variable resistor is increased?

....

c) Calculate the **current** in the circuit when the resistance of the variable resistor is **1 Ω**.

....

....

Parallel Circuits

Q1 Tick to show whether these statements about parallel circuits are **true** or **false**.

                                                                        True False

a) Components are connected side-by-side (instead of end-to-end). ☐ ☐

b) Each component has the same potential difference across it. ☐ ☐

c) The current is the same everywhere in the circuit. ☐ ☐

d) Components can be switched on and off independently. ☐ ☐

Q2 The diagrams show currents at junctions in two parallel circuits.

Write in the **missing** values.

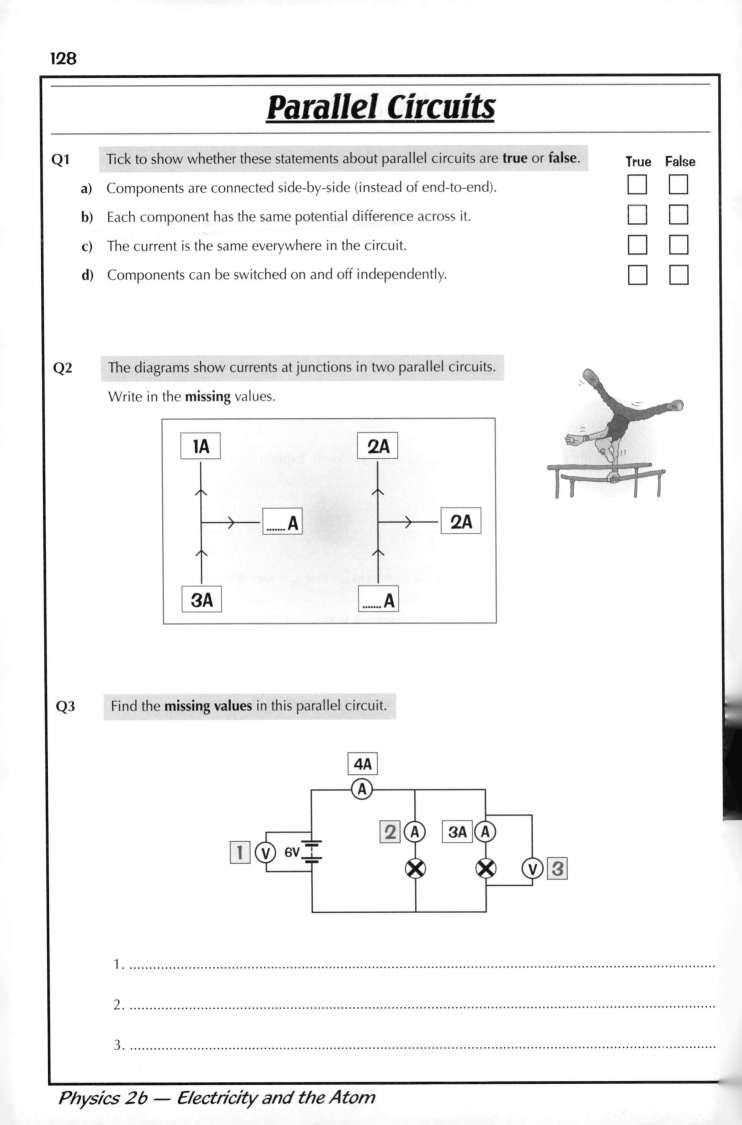

Q3 Find the **missing values** in this parallel circuit.

1. ....

2. ....

3. ....

Parallel Circuits

Q4 Karen does an experiment with different numbers of lamps in a parallel circuit. The diagrams below show her three circuits.

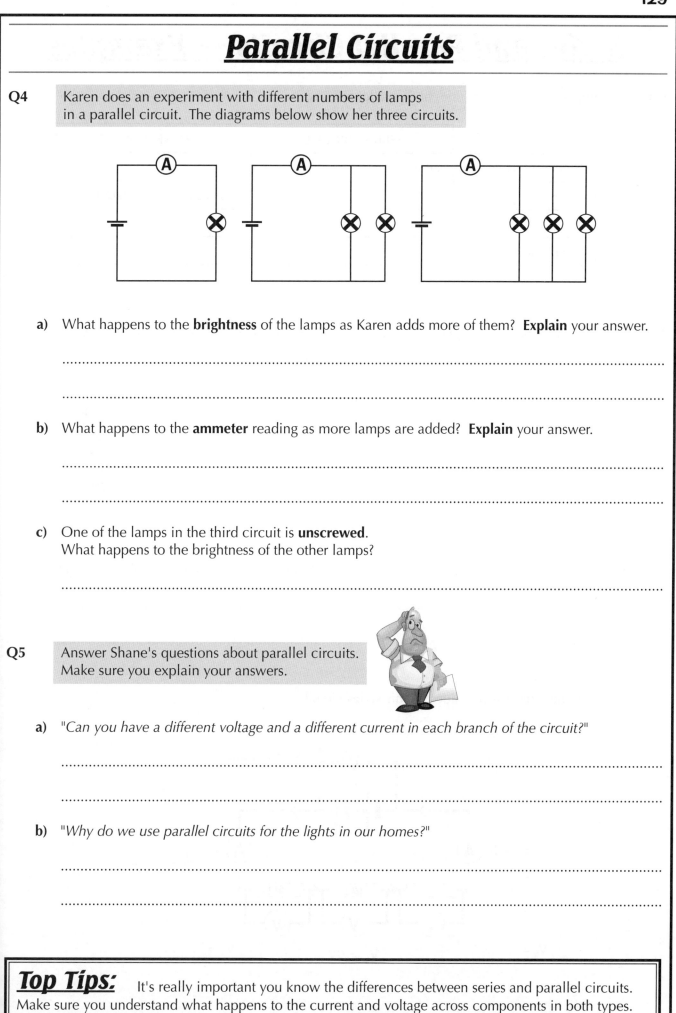

a) What happens to the **brightness** of the lamps as Karen adds more of them? **Explain** your answer.

....

....

b) What happens to the **ammeter** reading as more lamps are added? **Explain** your answer.

....

....

c) One of the lamps in the third circuit is **unscrewed**.
What happens to the brightness of the other lamps?

....

Q5 Answer Shane's questions about parallel circuits.
Make sure you explain your answers.

a) *"Can you have a different voltage and a different current in each branch of the circuit?"*

....

....

b) *"Why do we use parallel circuits for the lights in our homes?"*

....

....

Top Tips: It's really important you know the differences between series and parallel circuits.
Make sure you understand what happens to the current and voltage across components in both types.

Series and Parallel Circuits — Examples

Q1 **Complete** this table for series and parallel circuits:

	SERIES CIRCUITS	PARALLEL CIRCUITS
Components connected	end to end	
Current		can be different in each branch
Voltage	shared between components	
Example of use		

Q2 A set of **Christmas tree lights** is designed to work on mains voltage (230 V). It has **12 V** bulbs.

a) How can you tell that these lights are wired in series?

....

....

b) Why might it be better to wire Christmas tree lights in **parallel**?

....

....

c) Give one reason why you can't usually swap bulbs between series and parallel sets of lights.

....

....

Q3 Fill in the **four** missing values on this **series** circuit:

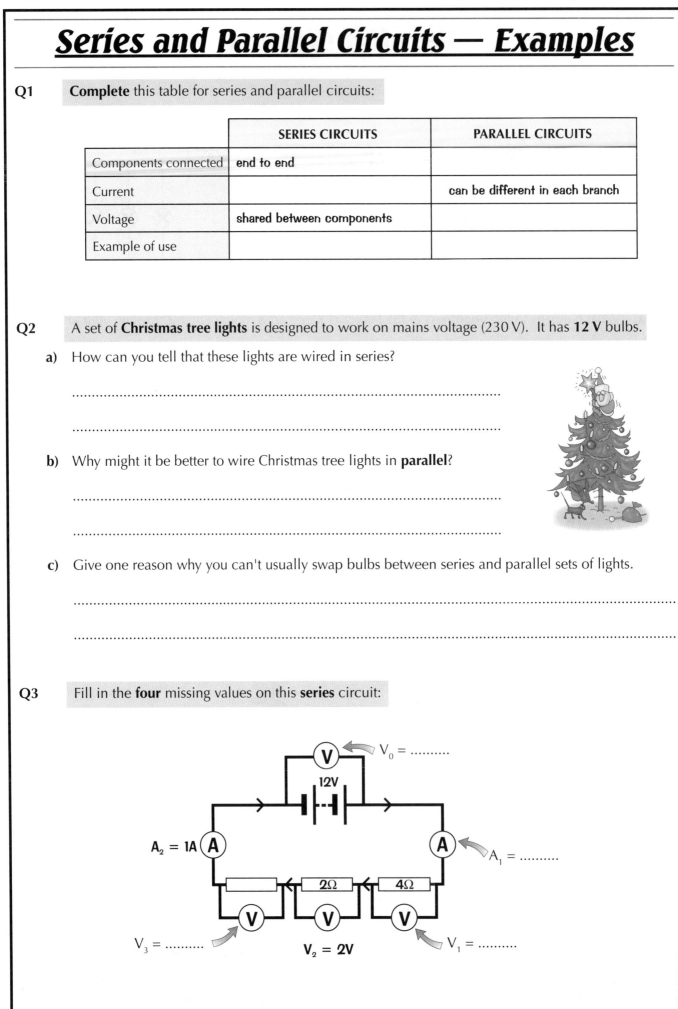

V_0 = ...

12V

A_2 = 1A

A_1 = ...

2Ω   4Ω

V_3 = ... V_2 = 2V V_1 = ...

Series and Parallel Circuits — Examples

Q4 The diagram opposite shows a **parallel** circuit.

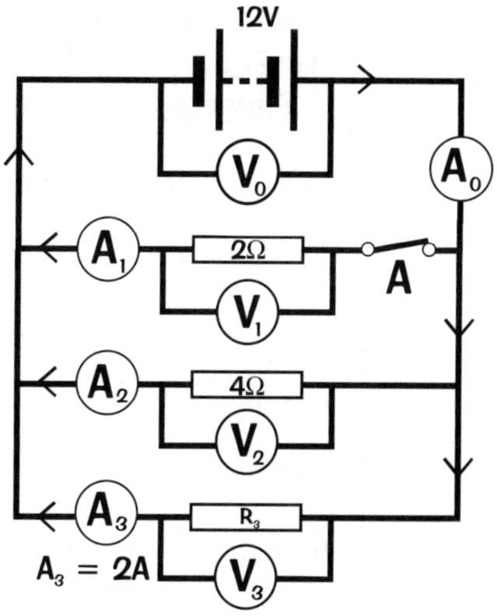

a) Calculate the readings on ammeters:

i) A_1 ....

ii) A_2 ....

b) Find the readings on voltmeters:

i) V_1 ....

ii) V_2 ....

c) What is the reading on ammeter A_0 when switch A is open?

....

....

Q5 A group of pupils make the following **observations**:

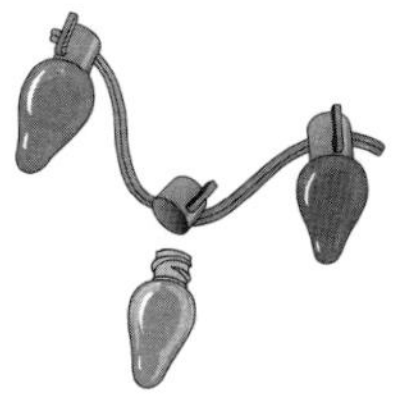

1. "The lights go dim if you switch the fan on in a parked car."

2. "You can switch Christmas tree lights off by unscrewing one of the bulbs."

3. "The lights in my house are wired in parallel, but all the wall lights in the living room go on and off together."

Explain their observations.

1. ....

....

....

2. ....

....

....

3. ....

....

....

....

Think about what makes them go on and off.

Mains Electricity

Q1   Choose from the words below to fill in the gaps.

changing	batteries	hertz	d.c.	volts	direct
alternating	a.c.	same	frequency	amps	direction

In the United Kingdom the mains electrical supply is about 230 ....

The supply is .... current (...............) which means that the

.... of the current is constantly .... The supply

has a .... of 50 cycles per second (50 ....).

Cells and .... supply .... current (...............) —

the current always passes in the .... direction.

Q2   The diagram shows three traces on the same CRO. The settings are the same in each case.

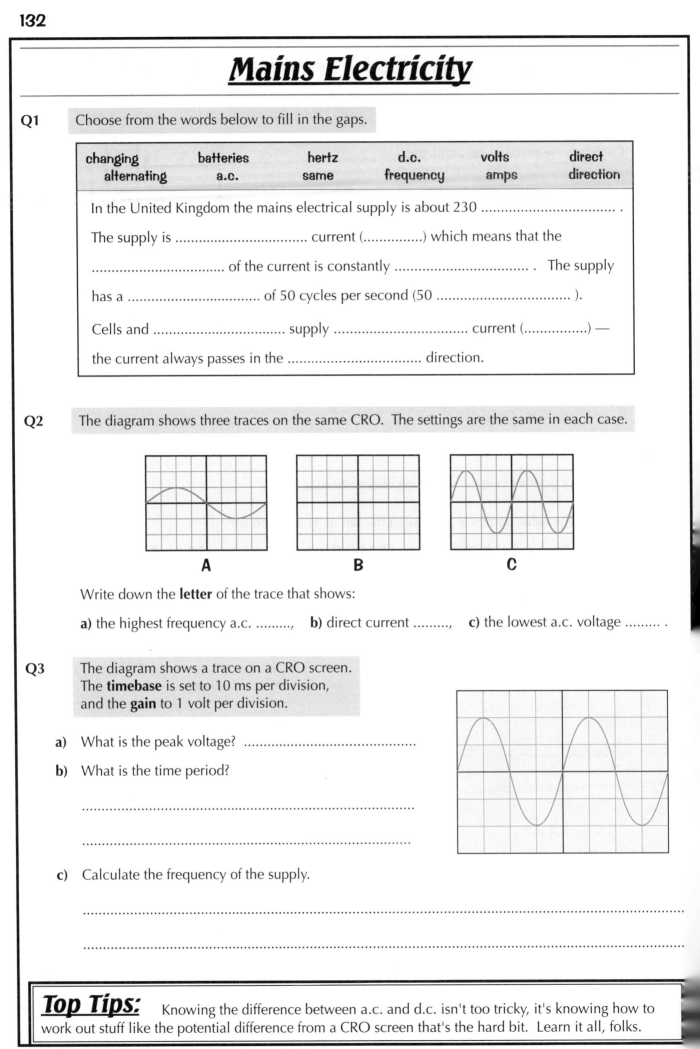

A   **B**   **C**

Write down the **letter** of the trace that shows:

a) the highest frequency a.c. ...., **b)** direct current ...., **c)** the lowest a.c. voltage ....

Q3   The diagram shows a trace on a CRO screen.
The **timebase** is set to 10 ms per division,
and the **gain** to 1 volt per division.

a) What is the peak voltage? ....

b) What is the time period?

....

....

c) Calculate the frequency of the supply.

....

....

Electricity in the Home

Q1   Look at this picture of a kitchen. Put a **ring** round everything that is **unsafe**.

Q2   Answer the following questions about **plugs**:

a)   Why is the body of a plug made of rubber or plastic?

....

b)   Explain why some parts of a plug are made from copper or brass.

....

c)   What material is the cable insulation made from, and why?

....

Q3   Use the words below to complete these rules for wiring a plug.

   outer   bare   live   earth   neutral   insulation   firmly   green and yellow

a)   Strip the .... off the end of each wire.

b)   Connect the brown wire to the .... terminal.

c)   Connect the blue wire to the .... terminal.

d)   Connect the .... wire to the .... terminal.

e)   Check all the wires are .... screwed in with no .... bits showing.

f)   The cable grip must be securely fastened over the .... covering of the cable.

Q4   This plug is **incorrectly** wired. Write down the **three** mistakes.

   = Neutral
   = Live
   = Earth

   1. ....
   2. ....
   3. ....

Physics 2b — Electricity and the Atom

Fuses and Earthing

Q1 **Match** up the beginnings and endings of these sentences:

The live and neutral wires...	... should be connected to the earth wire.
A circuit breaker...	... should normally carry the same current.
A Residual Current Circuit Breaker...	... does the same job as a fuse.
Any metal casing...	... can be used instead of a fuse and earth wire.
A fuse melts when the current...	... in a fuse wire exceeds the rating of the fuse.

Q2 Put these events in the correct order to describe what happens when a fault occurs in an earthed kettle. Label the events from 1 to 4.

☐ The device is isolated from the live wire.   ☐ A big current flows out through the earth wire.

☐ A big surge in current blows the fuse.   ☐ A fault allows the live wire to touch the metal case.

Q3 Some circuits are protected by Residual Current Circuit breakers (RCCBs).

a) Briefly describe how an RCCB works.

....

....

b) Give two advantages of using RCCBs instead of fuses.

1. ....

2. ....

Q4 A **'double insulated'** hair dryer uses a current of 0.25 A.

a) Andrea has fuses rated 0.25 A, 2 A and 8 A.
Which fuse should she fit in the plug for the hair dryer?   ....

b) Why does the hair dryer **not** need an **earth wire**?

....

c) What type of electrical cable will the hair dryer have? Circle the correct answer.

two-core cable   **three-core cable**

d) Andrea notices the electrical supply cable for her TV is much thicker than for her hair dryer. Explain how **cable thickness** and **fuse ratings** of appliances are **linked**.

....

....

Physics 2b — Electricity and the Atom

Energy and Power in Circuits

Q1 Fill in the gaps using the words in the box.

power	energy	more	heat	how long	time

The energy transferred by an appliance depends on .... it's used

for and its .... The power of an appliance can be calculated

using the formula: power = ... ÷ ....

Whenever an electrical current flows through anything with an electrical resistance,

electrical energy is converted into .... energy. The less energy

wasted, e.g. as heat by an appliance, the .... efficient it is.

Q2 Raj is comparing **three** different types of light bulb. Below is a summary of his findings.

	Fluorescent bulb	Light-emitting diode (LED) bulb	Filament bulb
Energy efficiency	~10%	~75%	~2%
Cost	£3.50	£25	50p

a) Suggest **one** reason why the filament bulb has a low efficiency.

....

b) Give **one** reason why Raj might choose to buy the **LED** bulb rather than the other two types.

....

c) Suggest why Raj might choose to buy the filament bulb rather than the other two types.

....

....

Q3 Calculate the **amount** of electrical energy used by the following.
For each component, say what **forms** of energy the electrical energy is converted to.

a) A 100 watt lamp in 10 seconds: .... J.

Electrical energy is converted to .... and .... energy.

b) A 500 watt motor in 2 minutes: .... J.

Electrical energy is converted to ...., ... and .... energy.

c) A 1 kW heater in 20 seconds: .... J.

Electrical energy is converted to .... energy.

d) A 2 kW heater in 10 minutes: .... J.

Remember to put time in seconds and power in W.

Electrical energy is converted to .... energy.

Power and Energy Change

Q1   Lucy is comparing **three lamps**. She connects each lamp in a circuit and measures the **current**. Her results are shown in the table below.

	Lamp A	Lamp B	Lamp C
Voltage (V)	12	3	230
Current (A)	2.5	4	0.1
Power (W)			
Energy used in one minute (J)			

a)   Complete the table by filling in the missing values.

b)   What rating of fuse would each lamp need?

A = ...,   B = ...,   C = ...

Typical fuse ratings are 1, 2, 3, 5, 7, 10 or 13A.

Q2   An electric heater is rated at **230 V, 1500 W**.

a)   Calculate the current it uses.

....

....

b)   What rating of fuse should be used with this heater? Circle your choice.

1 A   2 A   3 A   5 A   7 A   10 A   13 A

Q3   Henry is comparing two electric drills. He takes the measurements shown in the table below. Calculate the **missing values** and write them in the table.

	Drill A	Drill B
Current through drill (A)	2	3
Voltage drop across drill (V)	230	230
Charge passing in 5 s (C)		
Energy transformed in 5 s (J)		

Remember, current = charge ÷ time.

Q4   Tim's toy boat has a motor attached to a **2 V** battery. A current of **0.6 A** runs through the boat when it's switched on. Tim turns his boat on and leaves it running in his bath for **12 minutes**.

a)   Calculate the total charge passed.

....

b)   Calculate the energy transformed by the motor.

....

Atomic Structure

Q1   **Complete** the following sentences.

a)   Neutral atoms have .... charge.

b)   A charged atom is called an ....

c)   A neutral atom has the same number of .... and ....

d)   If an electron is removed from a neutral atom, the atom becomes .... charged.

Q2   **Complete** this table.

Particle	Mass	Charge
Proton	1	
	1	0
Electron		−1

Q3   In the early 1900s, the '**plum pudding**' model of the atom was replaced by **Rutherford** and **Marsden's** nuclear model.

a)   i)   Briefly describe the **experiment** Rutherford and Marsden carried out.

....

....

ii) What did they **expect** to happen in the experiment?

....

....

b)   Rutherford and Marsden used the results from their experiments to disprove the **plum pudding model** and come up with the **nuclear model** of the atom. Describe the **results** of their experiment, and what they showed about the **structure of the atom**.

....

....

....

....

....

....

I'm a swimwear model.

Top Tips: Make sure you can explain how the results from Rutherford and Marsden's scattering experiments led to the 'plum pudding' model being replaced by the nuclear model of the atom.

Atoms and Radiation

Q1   Indicate whether these sentences are **true** or **false**.   **True False**

a)   The total number of neutrons in an atom is called the atomic number.   ☐ ☐

b)   The total number of protons and neutrons in an atom is called the mass number.   ☐ ☐

c)   Atoms of the same element with the same number of neutrons are called isotopes.   ☐ ☐

d)   Radioactive decay speeds up at higher temperatures.   ☐ ☐

e)   Radioactive decay is a random process — you can't predict when it will happen.   ☐ ☐

Q2   **Radiation doses** are measured in **Sieverts (Sv)**.

a)   While you are reading this you are receiving about 2 mSv/year.

  i) What is causing this?

  ....

  ii) Suggest two **man-made** sources that might contribute to this radiation.

  1. ....

  2. ....

b)   The table below shows some typical radiation doses.

	Dose in Sv
50% survival probability, whole body dose	4 (single dose)
Legal worker dose limit (whole body)	0.02 per year
Average dose from all sources in Cornwall	0.008 per year
Average dose from natural radiation	0.002 per year
Average dose from a UK to Spain flight	0.00001 (single dose)

  i) Suggest why people living in Cornwall have a higher than normal dose.

  ....

  ii) Give **one** other natural source of background radiation.

  ....

  iii) A British pilot flies to Spain **and back** 500 times per year. If he
       lives in Cornwall, is his annual dose below the legal worker limit?

  ....

Ionising Radiation

Q1   Match up each description with the correct type of radiation.

Alpha particle   2 neutrons and 2 protons — the same as a helium nucleus.

Beta particle   A type of electromagnetic radiation.

Gamma radiation   An electron from the nucleus.

Q2   Complete the table below by choosing the correct word from each column.

Radiation Type	Ionising power weak/ moderate/ strong	Charge positive/ none/ negative	Relative mass no mass/ small/large	Penetrating power low/moderate/ high	Range in air short/long/ very long
alpha					
beta					
gamma					

Q3   Write the nuclear equations for the following decay processes.

a)   An atom of thorium-234 ($^{234}_{90}$Th) emits a beta particle and becomes an atom of protactinium (Pa).

....

b)   An atom of radon-222 ($^{222}_{86}$Rn) emits an alpha particle and becomes an atom of polonium (Po).

....

Q4   The diagram to the right shows the paths of an alpha particle and beta particle in an **electric field**.

Identify **two** ways in which the path of the alpha and beta particle differ and **explain** the reason for each difference.

1. ....

....

....

2. ....

....

Half-Life

Q1   A radioactive isotope has a half-life of **60 years**.
Which of these statements describes this isotope correctly? Tick one box only.

In 60 years, half of the atoms in the material will have gone. ☐

In 30 years' time, only half the atoms will be radioactive. ☐

In 60 years' time, the count rate will be half what it is now. ☐

In about 180 years there will be almost no radioactivity left in the material. ☐

Q2   The half-life of strontium-90 is **29 years**.

a)   What does this tell you will have happened to a pure sample of strontium-90 in 29 years' time?

....

b)   If you start with 1000 atoms of strontium-90, how many would you expect there to be after 87 years?

....

Q3   The activity of a radioactive sample is **1440 cpm**. 5 hours later
it has fallen to **45 cpm**. What is the half-life of this material?

....

....

Q4   Sandra measures how the radioactivity of a sample changes with time.
The table shows some of her results.

Time (minutes)	0	10	20	30	40	80	160
Counts per minute	740	553	420	326	260	140	103

a)   Use Sandra's results to draw a graph of
counts per minute against time.

b)   The counts per minute will never fall below 100.
Suggest two reasons why.

....

....

c)   Sandra calculates that the half-life of her sample is
about 20 minutes. Explain how she worked this out.
(You may find it useful to show some of the working on your graph.)

....

....

Uses of Radiation

Q1   The following sentences explain how a smoke detector works, but they are in the wrong order.

Put them in order by labelling them 1 (first) to 6 (last).

- [ ] The circuit is broken so no current flows.
- [1] The radioactive source emits alpha particles.
- [ ] A current flows between the electrodes — the alarm stays off.
- [ ] The alarm sounds.
- [ ] The air between the electrodes is ionised by the alpha particles.
- [ ] A fire starts and smoke particles absorb the alpha radiation.

Q2   The diagram shows how radiation can be used to sterilise surgical instruments.

radioactive source

thick lead

a) What kind of radioactive source is used, and why? In your answer, mention the **type** of radiation emitted (α, β and γ) and the **half-life** of the source.

....

....

b) What is the purpose of the thick lead?

....

Q3   The table shows the properties of three radioactive isotopes.

Radioactive isotope	Half-life	Type of emission
technetium-99	6 hours	beta/gamma
phosphorus-32	14 days	beta
cobalt-60	5 years	beta/gamma

a) Which isotope would be best to use as a medical tracer and why?

....

....

....

b) Which isotope would a hospital use to treat cancer patients? Explain your answer.

....

....

Top Tips: As well as being able to say which radioactive source is the best to use for a particular job, you've also got to be able to say why it's the best. You've got to think about stuff like the type of radiation it emits and what the half-life of the source is. Lots to think about folks.

Radioactivity Safety

Q1 Two scientists are handling samples of radioactive material.

a) One of the scientists is taking sensible safety precautions, but the other is not.
Describe three things which the careless scientist is doing wrong.

1...

2...

3...

b) Describe another way the scientists can reduce their exposure to the radiation,
without using special apparatus or clothing.

....

....

c) How should radioactive samples be stored when they are not in use?

....

Q2 The three different types of radiation can all be dangerous.

a) Which **two** types of radiation can pass through the human body?
Circle the correct answers.

    alpha   beta   gamma

b) i) Which type of radiation is usually most dangerous if it's inhaled or swallowed?

....

ii) What effects can this type of radiation have on the human body?

....

....

....

Top Tips: You should always handle radioactive sources really carefully. People who work
with radioisotopes often wear **dosimeters** — badges which record their exposure.

Physics 2b — Electricity and the Atom

Nuclear Fission and Fusion

Q1 Choose from the following words to complete the passage.

split	chemical	turbine	electricity	uranium-235	water	wine
	steam	moped	generator	reactors	heat	

Inside a nuclear reactor, ... (or plutonium-239) atoms

.... and release .... energy. This energy

is used to turn .... into ....

The steam then turns a ...., which in turn drives a

................................., producing ....

Q2 Explain how a nuclear fission **chain reaction** occurs, starting with a single **plutonium** nucleus absorbing a **slow-moving neutron**.

....

....

....

....

Q3 List four differences between nuclear **fission** and nuclear **fusion**.

1..

2..

3..

4..

Q4 Give two good points and two bad points about **fusion reactors**.

Good points ....

....

Bad points ....

....

The Life Cycle of Stars

Q1 Complete the passage, choosing from the words given below.

| gravity | millions | hot | fusion | stable | inwards | outwards | billions | fission | mass |

When a protostar gets .... enough, hydrogen nuclei will start to undergo

nuclear .... and the star enters its .... phase (becoming

a main sequence star). The force from the heat generated inside the star (pushing

...............................) and the force of gravity (pushing ....) are balanced.

The star might stay in this stable phase for .... of years.

Q2 Stars are formed from clouds of dust and gas.

a) **Why** does the material come together?

....

b) Describe how a **planets** can form around a star.

....

....

Q3 Towards the end of its life, a **main sequence** star will become a **red giant**.

a) What causes a star to become a **red giant**?

....

....

b) Why is a red giant **red**?

....

c) What happens to **small stars** like our Sun after they become red giants?

....

....

Q4 Some red giants start to undergo **more fusion reactions**, glow very brightly and then **explode**.
Give the **name** of this explosion, and describe what happens after it.

....

....

....

....

The Life Cycle of Stars

Q5   Below is a diagram showing the **life cycle** of **stars**.

Clouds of Dust and Gas
Red Giant
Neutron Star
Protostar
Black Hole
Main Sequence Star
Black Dwarf
White Dwarf
Supernova
Red Super Giant

Match the letters to the words on the right of the diagram.

A ....   B ....

C ....   D ....

E ....   F ....

G ....   H ....

I ....   J ....

Q6   The early universe only contained the element **hydrogen**.

a)   Why does the universe now contain lots of different elements?

....

b)   How are main sequence stars able to maintain their energy output for millions of years?

....

c)   Stars form heavy elements such as iron during their stable phases.
      Describe how elements **heavier** than iron are created and **spread out** throughout the universe.

....

....

....

....

Mixed Questions — Physics 2b

Q1   The table gives information about four different **radioactive isotopes**.

a)   Explain how the atomic structure of cobalt-60 is different from the structure of 'normal' cobalt-59.

Source	Type of Radiation	Half-life
radon-222	alpha	3.8 days
technetium-99m	gamma	6 hours
americium-241	alpha	432 years
cobalt-60	beta and gamma	5.27 years

....

....

b)   Which sources in the table would be most suitable for each of the uses below?

       medical tracers   **smoke detectors**   **detecting leaks in pipes**

     ....

c)   Radiation can be used to treat cancer.

    i)   What type of radiation is used in this treatment? ....

    ii)   Explain why patients often feel very ill while receiving this treatment.

     ....

d)   Jim measures the count rate of a sample of americium-241 as 120 cpm.
Roughly how long would it take for the count rate to fall below **4 cpm**? Show your working.

    ....

    ....

e)   Give one precaution Jim should take while handling the radioactive sample.

    ....

Q2   The diagram shows a circuit in which three resistors are connected in series.

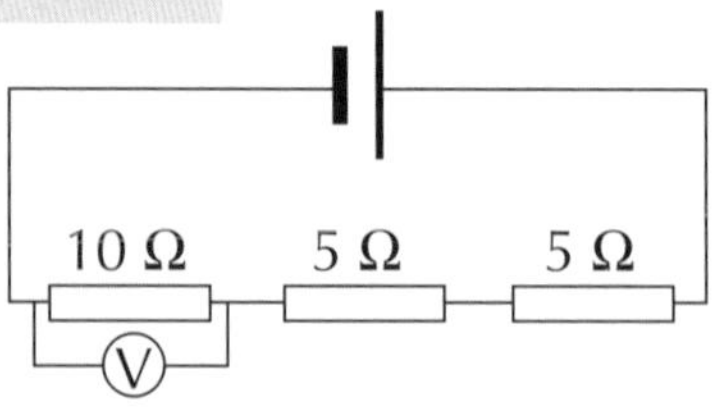

a)   Calculate the total resistance of the 3 resistors.

    ....

10 Ω   5 Ω   5 Ω

b)   If the voltmeter shown reads 4 V, find:

    i)   the current flowing in the circuit. ....

    ii)   the voltage of the power supply. ....

    ....

    iii) the energy dissipated in each of the 5 Ω resistors in 2 minutes.

    ....

    ....

Mixed Questions — Physics 2b

Q3   The diagram below shows part of a chain reaction in a nuclear reactor.

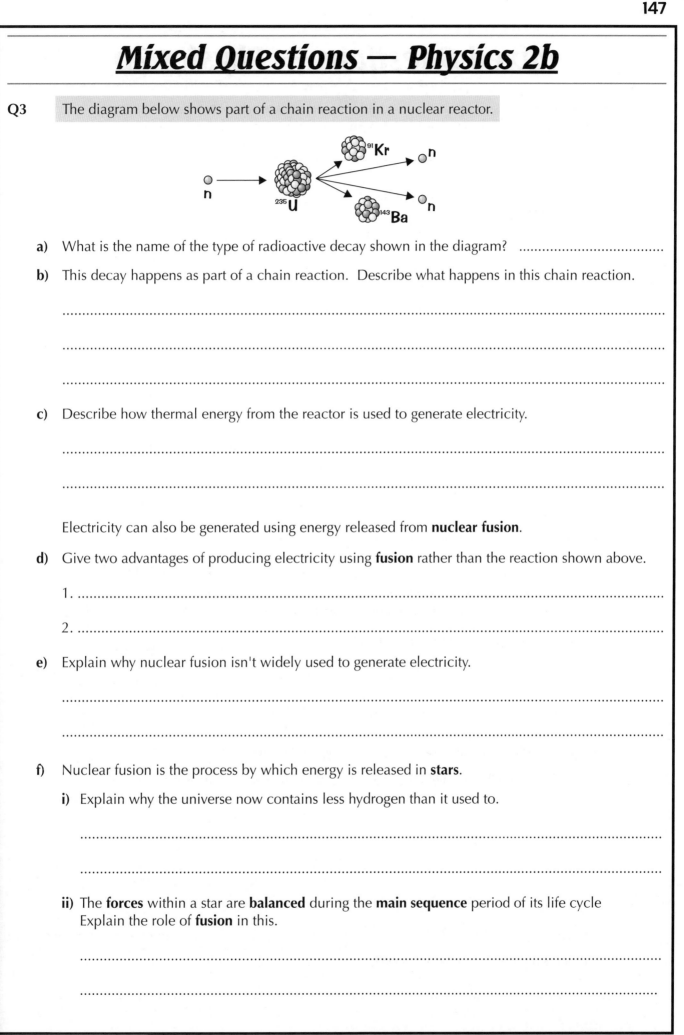

a) What is the name of the type of radioactive decay shown in the diagram? ....

b) This decay happens as part of a chain reaction. Describe what happens in this chain reaction.

....

....

....

c) Describe how thermal energy from the reactor is used to generate electricity.

....

....

Electricity can also be generated using energy released from **nuclear fusion**.

d) Give two advantages of producing electricity using **fusion** rather than the reaction shown above.

1. ....

2. ....

e) Explain why nuclear fusion isn't widely used to generate electricity.

....

....

f) Nuclear fusion is the process by which energy is released in **stars**.

i) Explain why the universe now contains less hydrogen than it used to.

....

....

ii) The **forces** within a star are **balanced** during the **main sequence** period of its life cycle
Explain the role of **fusion** in this.

....

....

Mixed Questions — Physics 2b

Q4 The diagram shows a circuit which could be used for the lights on a car.
Each headlight bulb is rated at 12 V, 6 A and each side light bulb is rated at 12 V, 0.5 A.

a) Calculate the total current flowing from the battery when:

i) Switch A is closed and switch B is open. ....

ii) Switch A is open and switch B is closed. ....

iii) Switches A and B are both closed. ....

b) The car has a **thermostat** to regulate temperature in the engine. Name the **type** of
resistor used in a thermostat and briefly **describe** how this type of resistor works.

....

....

c) A car battery supplies direct current (DC) but mains electricity is alternating current (AC).

The diagram shows a CRO trace from a mains electricity supply on the
island of Bezique. The **timebase** dial was set to 10 ms per large division.

Calculate the **frequency** of Bezique's electricity supply.

....

....

Q5 Modern electrical appliances are carefully designed to prevent the user getting an electric shock.

a) Tom's washing machine develops a fault. Part of the live wire touches the metal case.
Explain how the earth wire and fuse work together to prevent Tom getting an electric shock.

....

....

b) Bob buys a new 'double insulated' television set.

i) Which wires are in the plug?   ....

ii) What is meant by 'double insulated'?

....

GCSE
Additional Science

Exam Board: AQA

Fully updated for the
New GCSE courses

Answer Book

Higher Level

Contents

Published by CGP

ISBN: 978 1 84762 761 2

Groovy website: www.cgpbooks.co.uk

Printed by Elanders Ltd, Newcastle upon Tyne.
Jolly bits of clipart from CorelDRAW®

Based on the classic CGP style created by Richard Parsons.

Biology 2a — Cells, Organs and Populations

Biology 2a — Cells, Organs and Populations

Page 1 — Cells

Q1 a) Plant, animal
b) cell wall
c) Both plant and animal cells, proteins
d) membrane
Q2 a) The **nucleus** contains genetic material / chromosomes / genes / DNA. Its function is controlling the cell's activities.
b) **Chloroplasts** contain chlorophyll. Their function is to make food by photosynthesis.
c) The **cell wall** is made of cellulose. Its function is to support the cell and strengthen it.
Q3 a) animal
b) E.g.

c) Respiration happens inside mitochondria, which provides energy for life processes.
Q4 a) cell wall
b) cell membrane
c) cytoplasm
d) Because the genetic material is floating in the cytoplasm and not in a nucleus.

Pages 2-3 — Diffusion

Q1 random, higher, lower, net, bigger, gases
Q2 a)

(The dye particles will have spread out evenly.)
b) The rate of diffusion would **speed up**.
c) The dye particles will move from an area of higher concentration (the drop of dye) to an area of lower concentration (the water).
Q3 a) Switching a fan on will spread the curry particles more quickly through the house.
b) The curry will smell stronger. Adding more curry powder increases the concentration of the curry particles and increases the rate of diffusion of the curry particles to the air.
Q4 a) False
b) False
c) True
d) True
e) False
Q5 a) B
b) There is a greater concentration difference between the two sides of the membrane in model B so the molecules will diffuse faster.
Q6 a) glucose
b) Starch molecules are too large to fit through the pores in the membrane, but the small glucose molecules would diffuse through to the area of lower glucose concentration outside the bag.

Page 4 — Specialised Cells

Q1 a) red blood cells
b) sperm cell
c) guard cells
d) egg cell / ovum

Q2 Lots of chloroplasts... for photosynthesis.
Tall shape... gives a large surface area for absorbing CO_2.
Thin shape... means you can pack more cells in at the top of the leaf.
Q3 stomata, turgid, photosynthesis, flaccid, night.
Q4 a) Concave discs / biconcave discs
b) It gives them a large surface area for absorbing oxygen.
c) To leave even more room for haemoglobin / carrying oxygen.
Q5 a) Sperm
b) Sperm
c) Egg
d) Sperm
e) Sperm

Pages 5-6 — Cell Organisation

Q1

Cell	Tissue	Organ	Organ System	Organism
sperm egg (human) white blood cell	blood muscle	stomach eye heart liver small intestine	digestive system reproductive system excretory system	snail cat dog

Q2 a) True
b) False
c) True
d) True
e) True
f) False
g) True
Q3 epithelial cells, epithelial tissue, stomach, digestive system, human
Q4 a) materials, nutrients, bile, organs, liver, tissues, muscular tissue, churn
b) It makes digestive juices that digest food.
c) E.g. pancreas, salivary glands.
Q5 a) To exchange and transport materials.
b) The process by which cells become specialised for a particular job.
Q6 a) A group of similar cells that work together to carry out a particular function.
b) A group of different tissues that work together to perform a certain function.
c) A group of organs working together to perform a particular function.

Pages 7-8 — Plant Structure and Photosynthesis

Q1 water + carbon dioxide → glucose + oxygen
Q2 a) E.g. stems, roots, leaves
b) Mesophyll tissue — it's where most of the photosynthesis in a plant occurs.
Epidermal tissue — it covers the whole plant.
Xylem and phloem — it transports water, mineral ions and sucrose around the plant.
Q3 a) 00.00 (midnight)
b) There's no light at night so photosynthesis won't occur.
c) Plants use the food / glucose (from photosynthesis) they have stored during the day.
d)

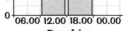

Q4 a) i) Gas A = carbon dioxide
Gas B = oxygen

Biology 2a — Cells, Organs and Populations

ii) As it gets lighter, the level of oxygen should increase as the plant will photosynthesise more and produce more oxygen. Carbon dioxide levels should decrease as light intensity increases, because the plant uses up carbon dioxide in photosynthesis.

b) i) As light intensity increases, the amount of carbon dioxide decreases.

ii) As light intensity increases, the amount of oxygen increases.

Q5 a) Plant B

b) The plant in the dark can't photosynthesise and so only has stored starch. The plant in sunlight is able to carry out photosynthesis and produce more glucose, which is then changed to more starch and stored in the leaves.

c) In the chloroplasts.

Pages 9-11 — The Rate of Photosynthesis

Q1 a) E.g. light intensity, CO_2 concentration, temperature

b) A factor that stops photosynthesis from happening any faster.

c) E.g. time of day (such as night time) / position of plant (such as in the shade).

Q2 a) It increases the rate of photosynthesis up to a certain point.

b) The rate of photosynthesis does not continue to increase because temperature or levels of carbon dioxide act as limiting factors.

Q3 a) blue light (approx. 440 nm), red light (approx. 660 nm)

b) You could use blue or red light bulbs to increase the rate of photosynthesis, and therefore the growth rate.

Q4 So that his plants grow well but so that he's not giving them more CO_2 than they need, as this would be wasting money.

Q5 a) the rate of photosynthesis

b)

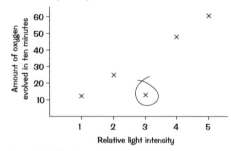

c) i) See circled point on graph.

ii) E.g. she might have counted bubbles for less time than 10 minutes / she might have accidentally used a lower light intensity / she might have miscounted.

d) The rate of photosynthesis increased as light intensity increased.

e) The relationship would continue up to a point, and then the graph would level off. At this point, either the temperature or carbon dioxide level would be acting as a limiting factor.

Q6 a) amount of light and temperature

b) The faster the rate of photosynthesis, the faster the growth rate of the grass.

Q7 a) Any three from, e.g: it traps heat to make sure temperature does not become a limiting factor. / Artificial light can be used to enable photosynthesis to occur at all times. / Carbon dioxide can be maintained at a high level. / Plants can be kept free from pests. / Fertilisers can be added to provide all the necessary minerals for healthy plant growth.

b) i) a heater / artificial light / insulation

ii) ventilation or shades

iii) artificial lights

iv) To produce carbon dioxide and so increase carbon dioxide levels in the greenhouse, thus increasing the rate of photosynthesis.

Q8 a)

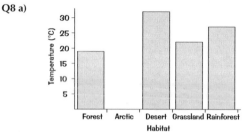

b) Arctic

c) The temperatures are extremely low there, so the rate of photosynthesis will be slower because the enzymes needed for photosynthesis will be working very slowly.

d) Despite the high temperatures, few plants grow in the desert because there is not enough water for them to survive.

Page 12 — How Plants Use Glucose

Q1 leaves, energy, convert, cells, cellulose, walls, lipids, margarine, cooking oil / cooking oil, margarine

Q2 a) nitrate ions

b) dhal — approx. 67%
steak — approx. 64%

c) Dhal, as it contains significantly more B vitamins, calcium and iron, than steak.

d) from plants

Q3 a) They change starch to glucose and use it for respiration to release energy for growth.

b) They use their leaves to make glucose by photosynthesis.

c) They store starch, which is insoluble, so they don't draw in loads of water and swell up as they would if they stored glucose.

Page 13 — Distribution of Organisms

Q1 a) True

b) False

c) True

Q2 Any three from, e.g: temperature / availability of water / availability of oxygen and carbon dioxide / availability of nutrients / amount of light.

Q3 a) A square frame enclosing a known area.

b) E.g. he could divide the field into a grid and use a random number generator to pick coordinates.

c) i) $(3 + 1 + 2 + 1 + 4 + 3 + 0 + 2) \div 8 = 2$ daisies per quadrat

ii) 0,1,1,2,2,3,3,4 so middle value (median) is 2

d) 5 600 x 2 = 11 200 daisies

Page 14 — More on the Distribution of Organisms

Q1 a) i) E.g.

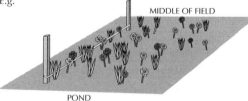

ii) E.g. she could collect data along the line by counting all the buttercups that touch it.

b) E.g. by having a larger sample size.

c) i) The number of buttercups decreases as you go further away from the pond.

ii) E.g. there is more water in the soil nearest to the pond, so more buttercups will grow there.

Q2 Bill's data isn't valid as it doesn't answer his question. The distribution of the dandelions could also be affected by the different soil moisture levels caused by the stream near the wood — he hasn't controlled all the variables.

Biology 2b — Enzymes and Genetics

Pages 15-17 — Mixed Questions — Biology 2a

Q1 Tissue — A group of similar cells that work together to carry out a certain function.
Diffusion — The spreading out of particles from an area of high concentration to an area of low concentration.
Habitat — The place where an organism lives.
Mode — The most common value in a set of data.
Photosynthesis — The process that produces 'food' (glucose) in plants and algae.
Limiting factor — Something that stops photosynthesis from happening any faster.
Differentiation — The process by which cells become specialised for a particular job.

Q2 a) chloroplasts, vacuole, cell wall

b) i)

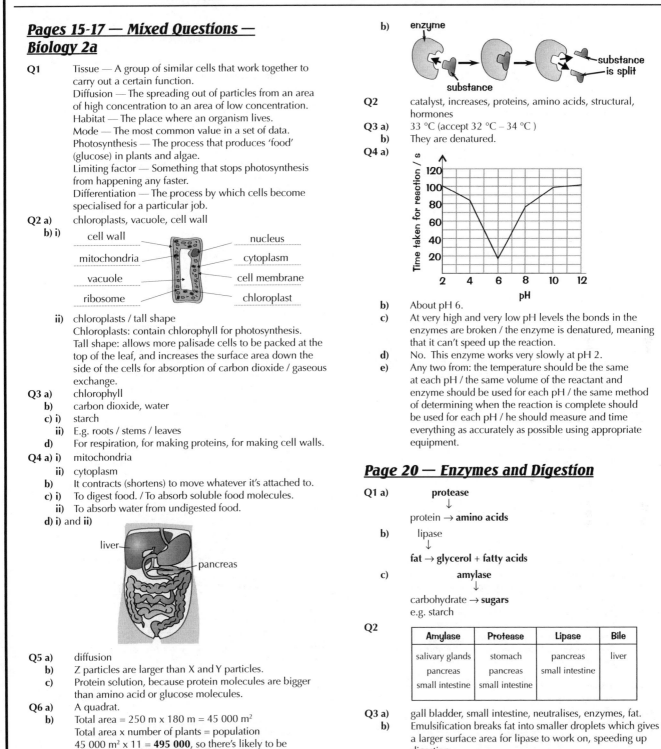

cell wall
nucleus
mitochondria
cytoplasm
vacuole
cell membrane
ribosome
chloroplast

ii) chloroplasts / tall shape
Chloroplasts: contain chlorophyll for photosynthesis.
Tall shape: allows more palisade cells to be packed at the top of the leaf, and increases the surface area down the side of the cells for absorption of carbon dioxide / gaseous exchange.

Q3 a) chlorophyll

b) carbon dioxide, water

c) i) starch

ii) E.g. roots / stems / leaves

d) For respiration, for making proteins, for making cell walls.

Q4 a) i) mitochondria

ii) cytoplasm

b) It contracts (shortens) to move whatever it's attached to.

c) i) To digest food. / To absorb soluble food molecules.

ii) To absorb water from undigested food.

d) i) and ii)

liver
pancreas

Q5 a) diffusion

b) Z particles are larger than X and Y particles.

c) Protein solution, because protein molecules are bigger than amino acid or glucose molecules.

Q6 a) A quadrat.

b) Total area = 250 m x 180 m = 45 000 m²
Total area x number of plants = population
45 000 m² x 11 = **495 000**, so there's likely to be approximately 500 000 clover plants.

c) i) (11 + 9 + 8 + 9 + 7) ÷ 5 = 8.8 plants

ii) (It is the same field, so use 45 000 m² again.)
45 000 m² x 8.8 = 396 000 clover plants (≈ 400 000).

d) Lisa's result is likely to be more accurate as she has used a larger sample size.

Biology 2b — Enzymes and Genetics

Pages 18-19 — Enzymes

Q1 a) Enzymes are biological catalysts.

b)

enzyme
substance
substance is split

Q2 catalyst, increases, proteins, amino acids, structural, hormones

Q3 a) 33 °C (accept 32 °C – 34 °C)

b) They are denatured.

Q4 a)

Time taken for reaction / s
120
100
80
60
40
20
2 4 6 8 10 12
pH

b) About pH 6.

c) At very high and very low pH levels the bonds in the enzymes are broken / the enzyme is denatured, meaning that it can't speed up the reaction.

d) No. This enzyme works very slowly at pH 2.

e) Any two from: the temperature should be the same at each pH / the same volume of the reactant and enzyme should be used for each pH / the same method of determining when the reaction is complete should be used for each pH / he should measure and time everything as accurately as possible using appropriate equipment.

Page 20 — Enzymes and Digestion

Q1 a)
protease
↓
protein → **amino acids**

b)
lipase
↓
fat → glycerol + fatty acids

c)
amylase
↓
carbohydrate → **sugars**
e.g. starch

Q2

Amylase	Protease	Lipase	Bile
salivary glands	stomach	pancreas	liver
pancreas	pancreas	small intestine	
small intestine	small intestine		

Q3 a) gall bladder, small intestine, neutralises, enzymes, fat.

b) Emulsification breaks fat into smaller droplets which gives a larger surface area for lipase to work on, speeding up digestion.

Page 21 — More on Enzymes and Digestion

Q1

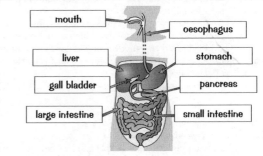

mouth
oesophagus
liver
stomach
gall bladder
pancreas
large intestine
small intestine

Biology 2b — Enzymes and Genetics

Q2 a) false
b) true
c) true
d) false
Q3 a) Produce saliva / amylase
b) Produces enzymes (protease, amylase and lipase) / releases enzymes into the small intestine.
c) Produces bile which emulsifies fats and neutralises stomach acid.

Page 22 — Enzymes and Respiration

Q1 a) glucose + oxygen → carbon dioxide + water (+ energy)
b) It means respiration that requires oxygen.
Q2 a) i) true
ii) false
iii) true
iv) false
v) true
vi) false
vii) true
viii) true
b) ii) Respiration usually releases energy from glucose.
iv) Respiration takes place in a cell's mitochondria.
vi) Breathing and respiration are completely separate processes.
Q3 E.g. building larger molecules from smaller ones, to allow muscles to contract (in animals), to maintain a certain body temperature (in mammals and birds) and to build sugars, nitrates and other nutrients into amino acids, which are then built up into proteins (in plants).

Pages 23-24 — Exercise

Q1 a) energy, contracting
b) glucose, oxygen
c) rapidly, glycogen
d) anaerobic
e) incomplete
Q2 a) Any two from: e.g. his breathing rate increases / he breathes more deeply / his heart rate increases.
b) i) muscle fatigue
ii) lactic acid
iii) anaerobic respiration
c) While John was respiring anaerobically he created an oxygen debt. When he stops exercising this must be repaid. To do this he breathes deeply to get the necessary oxygen into the muscles to oxidise the lactic acid.
Q3 a) Anaerobic: glucose → lactic acid (+ energy)
b) less
Q4 a) 45 – 15 = **30** breaths per minute
b) The breathing rate increases to provide more oxygen and glucose for increased respiration in the muscles, and to remove the extra carbon dioxide produced.
c) 3.5 minutes
Q5 a) Any two from, e.g: measuring their pulse rates by averaging over the same time period. / They should run the same distance. / They should run at the same speed.
b) Saeed

Pages 25-26 — Uses of Enzymes

Q1 a) Enzymes can be used to pre-digest baby food so that it is easier for babies to digest.
b) Enzymes can be used to convert glucose syrup into fructose syrup. Fructose is sweeter than glucose and so less has to be added to sweeten foods (which is good for slimmers).
Q2 a) Lipaclean would be best because it contains lipase enzymes and they digest fat.
b) Because they are allergic to them.
Q3 a) carbohydrates
b) isn't, is
c) carbohydrases
Q4 a) E.g. to speed up reactions.
b) Any two from: temperature, pH and lack of contamination.

c) i) Any two from: e.g you can use lower temperatures and pressures, which means a lower cost as it saves energy / enzymes are specific, so they only catalyse the reaction you want them to / they work for a long time so you can continually use them / they are biodegradable (so they cause less pollution).
ii) E.g. they can be denatured by a small change in temperature / they can be denatured by small changes in pH / they are susceptible to poisons / they can cause allergies / they can be expensive to produce.
Q5 a) E.g. use the same amount of each washing powder / use the same type of food stains / use clothes made of the same type of fabric.
b) i) Powder A
ii) Powder A. Biological detergents contain enzymes, so at low temperatures they work more effectively than other detergents.

Pages 27-28 — DNA

Q1 a) deoxyribose nucleic acid
b) cells, chromosomes, section, protein, amino acids
c) 20
d) double helix
e) No, identical twins have the same DNA.
Q2 1. Collect the sample for DNA testing.
2. Cut the DNA into small sections.
3. Separate the sections of DNA.
4. Compare the unique patterns of DNA.
Q3 a) E.g. DNA from a crime scene could be checked against everyone in the country.
b) E.g. it might be an invasion of privacy. / False positives could occur if there was a mistake in the analysis.
Q4

	Foal	Mother	Father
DNA sample	Sample 1	Sample 2	**Sample 4**

Q5 a) The victim and suspect A — they share a significant amount of their DNA.
b) Suspect B
c) Suspect B's DNA matches the DNA found at the crime scene.
d) No. If suspect B's blood was found on the victim's shirt, it doesn't mean that he/she committed the murder. Their blood could have got onto the shirt on a different occasion.

Page 29 — Cell Division — Mitosis

Q1 a) true
b) false (there are 23 pairs of chromosomes)
c) false (they're found in the nucleus)
d) true
e) true
f) true
g) true
Q2 a) Cells that are not dividing contain long strings of DNA.
b) Before a cell divides, it copies (duplicates) its DNA and forms X-shaped chromosomes.
c) The chromosomes line up across the centre of the cell, and then the arms of each chromosome are pulled to opposite ends of the cell.
d) A membrane forms in each half of the cell to form the nuclei.
e) The cytoplasm divides, making two new genetically identical cells.
Q3 reproduce, strawberry, runners, asexual, genes, variation.

Pages 30-31 — Cell Division — Meiosis

Q1 a) true
b) true
c) true
d) true
e) false

Biology 2b — Enzymes and Genetics

Q2 a) Before the cell starts to divide it duplicates its DNA to produce an exact copy.

b) For the first meiotic division the chromosomes line up in their pairs across the centre of the cell.

c) The pairs are pulled apart. Each new cell has only one copy of each chromosome, some from the mother and some from the father.

d) The chromosomes line up across the centre of the nucleus ready for the second division, and the left and right arms are pulled apart.

e) There are now 4 gametes, each containing half the original number of chromosomes.

Q3 a) two

b) 46, 23

c) different

d) half as many

Q4 a)

b)

Q5 a) Sex cells that only have one copy of each chromosome.

b) Gametes have half the usual number of chromosomes so that when two gametes join together during fertilisation the resulting fertilised egg will have the full number of chromosomes.

c) When two gametes fuse, the new individual will have a mixture of two sets of chromosomes — some from its mother and some from its father.

d) mitosis

Page 32 — Stem Cells

Q1 specialised, animal, plant, stem cells

Q2 Embryonic stem cells can differentiate into any type of body cell. Adult stem cells are less versatile — they can only turn into certain types of cell.

Q3 E.g. people with some blood diseases (e.g. sickle cell anaemia) can be treated by bone marrow transplants. Bone marrow contains stem cells that can turn into new blood cells to replace the faulty old ones.

Q4 diabetes — insulin-producing cells
paralysis — nerve cells
heart disease — heart muscle cells

Q5 a) E.g. stem cell research may lead to cures for a wide variety of diseases.

b) E.g. embryos shouldn't be used for experiments as each one is a potential human life.

Page 33 — X and Y Chromosomes

Q1 a) true

b) false

c) true

d) false

Q2 a)

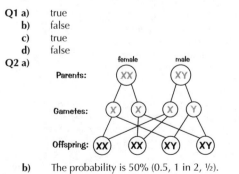

b) The probability is 50% (0.5, 1 in 2, ½).

Q3 a) ZW

b)

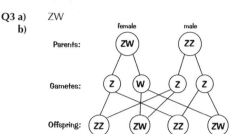

Page 34 — The Work of Mendel

Q1 monk, characteristics, generation, 1866, genetics.

Q2 a) E.g. hereditary units determine the characteristics of an organism. They're passed from parents to offspring. The modern word for them is genes.

b) The dominant hereditary unit is expressed.

Q3 a)

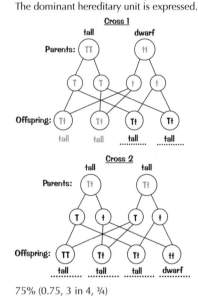

b) 75% (0.75, 3 in 4, ¾)

Pages 35-36 — Genetic Diagrams

Q1 dominant — shown in organisms heterozygous for that trait
genotype — the alleles that an individual contains
heterozygous — having two different alleles for a gene
homozygous — having two identical alleles for a gene
phenotype — the actual characteristics of an individual
recessive — not shown in organisms heterozygous for that trait

Q2 a) Wilma will have brown hair.

b) Wilma has two different alleles for this gene so she is heterozygous for the characteristic.

Q3 a) i) red eyes

ii) white eyes

iii) red eyes

iv) white eyes

b) i)

	parent's alleles	
	R	**r**
R	RR	Rr
r	Rr	rr

ii) 1/4 or 25%

iii) 12

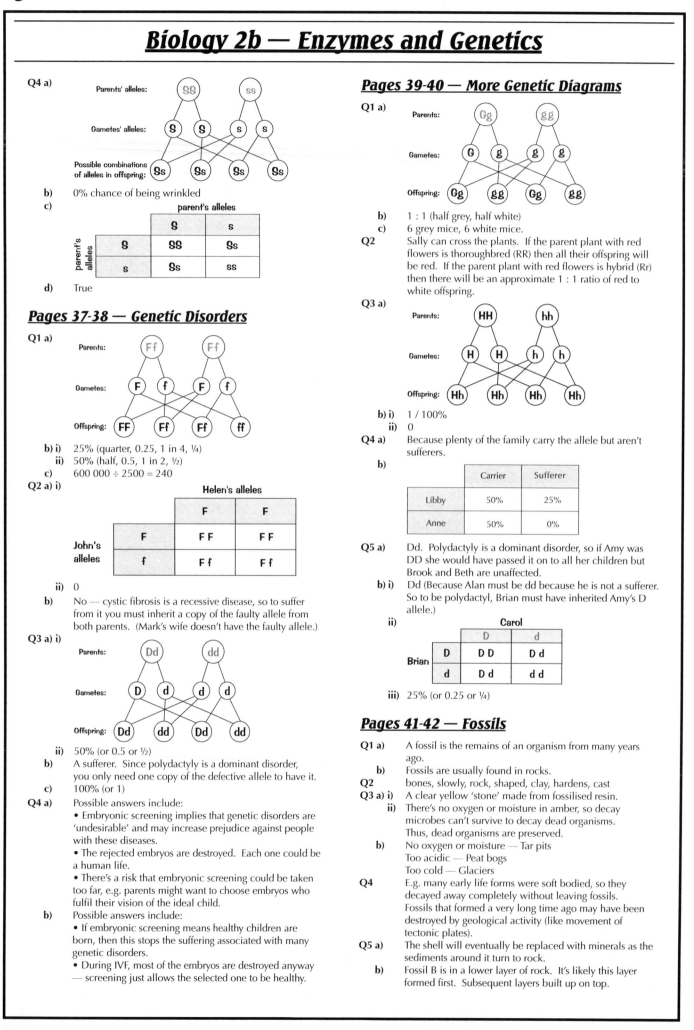

8

Biology 2b — Enzymes and Genetics

Q4 a)

Parents' alleles: SS ss

Gametes' alleles: S S s s

Possible combinations of alleles in offspring: Ss Ss Ss Ss

b) 0% chance of being wrinkled

c)

	parent's alleles	
	S	**s**
S	SS	Ss
s	Ss	ss

parent's alleles

d) True

Pages 37-38 — Genetic Disorders

Q1 a)

Parents: Ff Ff

Gametes: F f F f

Offspring: FF Ff Ff ff

b) i) 25% (quarter, 0.25, 1 in 4, ¼)
ii) 50% (half, 0.5, 1 in 2, ½)
c) 600 000 ÷ 2500 = 240

Q2 a) i)

		Helen's alleles	
		F	**F**
John's alleles	**F**	F F	F F
	f	F f	F f

ii) 0

b) No — cystic fibrosis is a recessive disease, so to suffer from it you must inherit a copy of the faulty allele from both parents. (Mark's wife doesn't have the faulty allele.)

Q3 a) i)

Parents: Dd dd

Gametes: D d d d

Offspring: Dd dd Dd dd

ii) 50% (or 0.5 or ½)
b) A sufferer. Since polydactyly is a dominant disorder, you only need one copy of the defective allele to have it.
c) 100% (or 1)
Q4 a) Possible answers include:
• Embryonic screening implies that genetic disorders are 'undesirable' and may increase prejudice against people with these diseases.
• The rejected embryos are destroyed. Each one could be a human life.
• There's a risk that embryonic screening could be taken too far, e.g. parents might want to choose embryos who fulfil their vision of the ideal child.
b) Possible answers include:
• If embryonic screening means healthy children are born, then this stops the suffering associated with many genetic disorders.
• During IVF, most of the embryos are destroyed anyway — screening just allows the selected one to be healthy.

Pages 39-40 — More Genetic Diagrams

Q1 a)

Parents: Gg gg

Gametes: G g g g

Offspring: Gg gg Gg gg

b) 1 : 1 (half grey, half white)
c) 6 grey mice, 6 white mice.
Q2 Sally can cross the plants. If the parent plant with red flowers is thoroughbred (RR) then all their offspring will be red. If the parent plant with red flowers is hybrid (Rr) then there will be an approximate 1 : 1 ratio of red to white offspring.

Q3 a)

Parents: HH hh

Gametes: H H h h

Offspring: Hh Hh Hh Hh

b) i) 1 / 100%
ii) 0
Q4 a) Because plenty of the family carry the allele but aren't sufferers.

b)

	Carrier	Sufferer
Libby	50%	25%
Anne	50%	0%

Q5 a) Dd. Polydactyly is a dominant disorder, so if Amy was DD she would have passed it on to all her children but Brook and Beth are unaffected.
b) i) Dd (Because Alan must be dd because he is not a sufferer. So to be polydactyl, Brian must have inherited Amy's D allele.)
ii)

		Carol	
		D	**d**
Brian	**D**	D D	D d
	d	D d	d d

iii) 25% (or 0.25 or ¼)

Pages 41-42 — Fossils

Q1 a) A fossil is the remains of an organism from many years ago.
b) Fossils are usually found in rocks.
Q2 bones, slowly, rock, shaped, clay, hardens, cast
Q3 a) i) A clear yellow 'stone' made from fossilised resin.
ii) There's no oxygen or moisture in amber, so decay microbes can't survive to decay dead organisms. Thus, dead organisms are preserved.
b) No oxygen or moisture — Tar pits
Too acidic — Peat bogs
Too cold — Glaciers
Q4 E.g. many early life forms were soft bodied, so they decayed away completely without leaving fossils.
Fossils that formed a very long time ago may have been destroyed by geological activity (like movement of tectonic plates).
Q5 a) The shell will eventually be replaced with minerals as the sediments around it turn to rock.
b) Fossil B is in a lower layer of rock. It's likely this layer formed first. Subsequent layers built up on top.

Chemistry 2a — Bonding and Calculations

Q6 a) A hypothesis.

b) It was so long ago that it's now very difficult to find any conclusive evidence for the hypothesis or against it.

c) E.g. another theory suggests that life began in a primordial swamp. Simple organic molecules joined to make more complex ones which eventually joined to give life forms.

Pages 43-44 — Extinction and Speciation

Q1 a) Extinct species are those that once lived but that don't exist any more.

b) We mainly know about extinct animals because we have found fossils of them. Also accept: We know more about some animals like mammoths because early people drew pictures of them, or about dodos because people wrote descriptions of them.

Q2 A catastrophic event kills every member of the species — A rare plant that lives on the side of a volcano is wiped out when the volcano erupts.

The environment changes too quickly — An island's rainforest is completely chopped down, destroying the habitat of the striped monkey.

A new disease kills every member of the species — Every member of a species of toad is killed when a new fungal pathogen is accidentally introduced to their habitat.

Q3 a) The development of a new species.

b) Because populations of the same species have become so different that they can't interbreed to give fertile offspring.

c) true

Q4 1 — There are two populations of the same species.

2 — Physical barriers separate the populations.

3 — The populations adapt to their new environments.

4 — A new species develops.

Q5 a) The spiders may have out-competed the squirrels for food (bananas).

b) The gibbons may have been a new predator and hunted the squirrels.

Q6 a) Isolation is where populations of a species are separated.

b) 1. A physical barrier geographically isolates some individuals from the main population.

2. Conditions on either side of a physical barrier are slightly different.

3. Each population shows variation because they have a wide range of alleles.

4. In each population, individuals with characteristics that make them better adapted to their environment have a better chance of survival and so are more likely to breed successfully.

5. The alleles that control the beneficial characteristics are more likely to be passed on to the next generation.

6. Eventually, individuals from the different populations have changed so much that they become separate species.

Pages 45-48 — Mixed Questions — Biology 2b

Q1 a) Stem cells have the ability to differentiate into different types of cell.

b) i) mitosis

ii) Stem cells from embryos can differentiate into all the different types of cells in the human body.

c) Possible answer: Some people feel that using embryos for stem cell research is unethical; they feel that every embryo has a right to life.

Q2 a) White flowers

b) i) FF

ii) ff

iii) Ff

c) 3 purple:1 white, because he is crossing two purple flowers which both have the alleles Ff.

Q3 Recessive, because the parents carry the allele but do not show the characteristics of albinism themselves.

Q4 a)

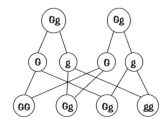

b) i) 3:1

ii) Because fertilisation is random, there is a 1 in 4 chance of each rabbit being white, but this is just a probability and the reality may be different.

c) All of their offspring will be white, because white rabbits are homozygous for the recessive allele (gg) and so cannot be carrying the allele for grey fur.

Q5 a) Fossil X

b) Most animals have hard parts in their bodies e.g. bones or shells. These parts are fossilised more easily.

c) If two organisms can reproduce and produce fertile offspring then they are of the same species. It is not possible to tell if two fossilised animals would have been able to do this.

Q6 a) E.g. her heart rate increased.

b) i) anaerobic respiration

ii) glucose → lactic acid (+ energy)

iii) She had an oxygen debt. She needed to breathe hard to get enough oxygen to oxidise the lactic acid.

c) i) amylase

ii) The salivary glands, the pancreas and the small intestine.

Q7 a) Really long molecules of DNA.

b) In humans, the males are XY and the females are XX.

Q8 a) The amount of DNA is doubling because the DNA is replicating itself.

b) The two daughter cells separate.

c) i) body cells

ii) asexual reproduction

d) E.g. mitosis involves one division whereas meiosis involves two divisions. / Mitosis produces two new cells whereas meiosis produces four new cells. / Mitosis produces identical cells whereas meiosis produces genetically different cells.

Chemistry 2a — Bonding and Calculations

Page 49 — Atoms, Compounds and Isotopes

Q1

Particle	Mass
Proton	1
Neutron	1
Electron	0

Q2 a)

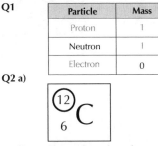

b) The total number of protons and neutrons in an atom.

c) compound

Q3 Isotopes, element, protons, neutrons.

Q4 W and Y, because these two atoms have the same number of protons but a different mass number.

Pages 50-51 — Ionic Bonding

Q1 a) i) true

ii) true

iii) false

iv) true

v) false

vi) true

Chemistry 2a — Bonding and Calculations

b) iii) E.g. atoms form ionic bonds to give them the same electronic structure as the noble gases.

v) E.g. in ionic bonding, electrons from the outer shell are transferred.

Q2 a) 2

b) 2

Q3 a) strong, positive, negative, all directions, large

b) Any two from: e.g. high boiling point / will dissolve to form solutions that conduct electricity when molten / will conduct electricity when molten

Q4 a) i) should be ticked

b) Sodium chloride has a cuboid shape because the electrostatic forces of attraction hold the oppositely charged ions together in a regular lattice arrangement.

Q5 a)

	Conducts electricity?
When solid	No
When dissolved in water	Yes
When molten	Yes

b) When solid, the ions are held tightly in a giant ionic lattice so they're unable to move and conduct electricity. When dissolved or molten, the ions are free to move and so can conduct electricity.

Page 52 — Ions and Formulas

Q1 a) Group 1

b) 1

c) 1$^+$

d) NaCl

Q2 non-metals, 1$^+$ charge, negative, 1$^-$ charge

Q3 BeS, K_2S, BeI_2, KI

Q4 a) KBr

b) $FeCl_2$

c) CaF_2

Page 53 — Electronic Structure of Ions

Q1 a)

b)

c)

Q2 a) $CaCl_2$

b)

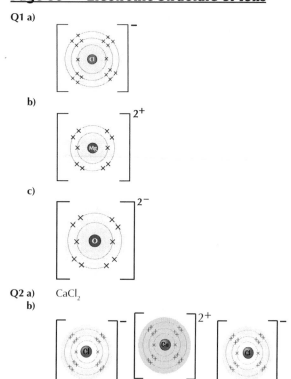

Pages 54-55 — Covalent Bonding

Q1 a) true

b) true

c) true

d) false

e) true

Q2

Atom	Carbon	Chlorine	Hydrogen	Nitrogen	Oxygen
Number of electrons needed to fill outer shell	4	1	1	3	2

Q3 Both atoms need to gain electrons. Sharing electrons allows both atoms to achieve the stable 'full outer shell' of electrons.

Q4 a)

b)

c)

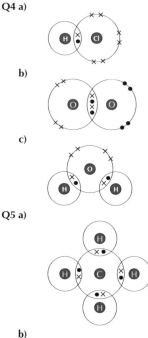

Q5 a)

b)

Q6 a) Atoms only share electrons in their outer energy levels/shells.

b) 1.

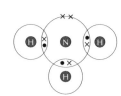

2.

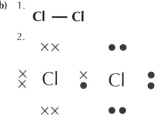

Pages 56-57 — Covalent Substances: Two Kinds

Q1 Diamond — I am used in drill tips; I am the hardest natural substance; My carbon atoms form four covalent bonds.
Graphite — I have layers which move over one another; I am used in pencils; I am a good conductor of electricity; My carbon atoms form three covalent bonds.
Silicon dioxide — I am also known as silica; I am not made from carbon.

Q2 atoms, strong, high

Q3 a) Any two from: e.g. low melting point / low boiling point / doesn't conduct electricity

Chemistry 2a — Bonding and Calculations

b) E.g. it has weak intermolecular forces so its molecules are easily parted from each other. / There are no ions so there's no electrical charge. / There are no ions to carry the current.

Q4 a) simple molecular and giant covalent/macromolecules
b) i) silicon dioxide
ii) graphite
iii) diamond
c) Any two from: e.g. it has a very high melting point. / It has a very high boiling point. / It doesn't conduct electricity.

Q5 a) i) Each carbon atom in graphite has one delocalised (free) electron. These free electrons conduct electricity.
ii) Graphite is made up of layers which are free to slide over each other. There are only weak intermolecular forces between the layers, so graphite is soft and slippery.
b) Each carbon atom forms four covalent bonds in a very rigid giant covalent structure.

Pages 58-59 — Metallic Structures

Q1 a) giant
b) heat
c) atoms
Q2 a) electrons, outer, strong, positive, regular
b) They have delocalised electrons which are free to move through the whole structure and conduct electricity.
Q3 a) An alloy is a mixture of two or more metals.
b) In pure metals the regular layers of atoms are able to slide over each other. This means they can be bent. However, in alloys there are atoms of more than one size. This distorts the layers and prevents them from being able to slide over each another. This makes brass harder than copper.
Q4 a) giant ionic
b) giant covalent
c) giant metallic
Q5

Property	Giant Ionic	Giant Covalent	Simple Molecular	Giant Metallic
High melting and boiling points	✓	✓	✗	✓
Can conduct electricity when solid	✗	✗ except graphite	✗	✓
Can conduct electricity when molten	✓	✗ except graphite	✗	✓

Q6 a) giant ionic — it only conducts electricity when molten or dissolved.
b) giant covalent — high melting point, but doesn't conduct electricity.
c) simple molecular — low melting point.
d) giant metallic — conducts electricity.

Pages 60-61 — New Materials

Q1 a) i) true
ii) false
iii) true
b) E.g. nitinol is affected by temperature.
c) It remembers its original shape — so if you bend it out of shape, you can heat it and it goes back to its 'remembered' shape.
d) E.g. dental braces / glasses frames
Q2 a) hundred, different
b) They have a huge surface area to volume ratio.
Q3 1 ÷ 0.000 001 = **1 000 000 nm**
Q4 a) fullerenes, molecules, hexagonal, atoms
b) Lightweight but strong — Building materials
Can detect specific molecules — Sensors to test water purity
Act like ball bearings to reduce friction — Lubricants for artificial joints
c) nanoscience
d) They are so small that they are absorbed more easily by the body than most particles.

Q5 a) They can conduct electricity.
b) The carbon atoms in nanotubes are joined by covalent bonds which makes them very strong.

Page 62 — Polymers

Q1 a) A
b) Thermosetting polymers have strong intermolecular forces called crosslinks between the polymer chains.
Q2 What the starting materials are and what the reaction conditions are.
Q3 a) LDP — toothpaste tubes need to be flexible so you can squeeze the paste out.
b) LDP — freezer bags also need to be flexible.
c) HDP — The equipment needs to have a high softening temperature so it can be sterilised by heating.

Page 63 — Relative Formula Mass

Q1 a) How heavy an atom of an element is compared to an atom of carbon-12.
b) i) 24
ii) 20
iii) 16
iv) 1
v) 12
vi) 63.5
vii) 39
viii) 40
ix) 35.5
Q2 Element A is helium
Element B is $(3 \times 4) = 12 =$ carbon
Element C is $(4 \times 4) = 16 =$ oxygen
Q3 a) You add the A_r of all the atoms in the compound together.
b) i) $(2 \times 1) + 16 = 18$
ii) $39 + 16 + 1 = 56$
iii) $1 + 14 + (3 \times 16) = 63$
iv) $(2 \times 1) + 32 + (4 \times 16) = 98$
v) $14 + (4 \times 1) + 14 + (3 \times 16) = 80$
Q4 $2XOH + H_2 = 114$
$2 \times (X + 16 + 1) + (2 \times 1) = 114$
$2 \times (X + 17) + 2 = 114$
$2 \times (X + 17) = 112$
$X + 17 = 56$
$X = 39$
so X = potassium

Page 64 — Two Formula Mass Calculations

Q1 a) Percentage mass of an element in a compound =
$\dfrac{A_r \times \text{No. of atoms (of that element)} \times 100}{M_r \text{ (of whole compound)}}$
b) i) $(14 \times 2) \div [14 + (4 \times 1) + 14 + (3 \times 16)] \times 100 = 35\%$
ii) $(4 \times 1) \div [14 + (4 \times 1) + 14 + (3 \times 16)] \times 100 = 5\%$
iii) $(3 \times 16) \div [14 + (4 \times 1) + 14 + (3 \times 16)] \times 100 = 60\%$
Q2 a) $A = (3 \times 16) \div [(2 \times 56) + (3 \times 16)] \times 100 = 30\%$
$B = 16 \div [(2 \times 1) + 16] \times 100 = 89\%$
$C = (3 \times 16) \div [40 + 12 + (3 \times 16)] \times 100 = 48\%$
b) B
Q3 a) $14 \div (14 + 16) \times 100 = 47\%$
b)

	Nitrogen	Oxygen
Percentage mass (%)	30.4	69.6
÷ A_r	$(30.4 \div 14) = 2.17$	$(69.6 \div 16) = 4.35$
Ratio	1	2

empirical formula = NO_2

Chemistry 2a — Bonding and Calculations

Q4

	Calcium	Oxygen	Hydrogen
Mass (g)	0.8	0.64	0.04
÷ A_r	$(0.8 ÷ 40) = 0.02$	$(0.64 ÷ 16) = 0.04$	$(0.04 ÷ 1) = 0.04$
Ratio	1	2	2

empirical formula = $Ca(OH)_2$ (or CaO_2H_2)

Pages 65-66 — Calculating Masses in Reactions

Q1 a) $2Mg + O_2 \rightarrow 2MgO$

b)
$2Mg$	$2MgO$
$2 × 24 = 48$	$2 × (24 + 16) = 80$
$48 ÷ 48 = 1$ g	$80 ÷ 48 = 1.67$ g
$1 × 10 = 10$ g	$1.67 × 10 = $ **16.7 g**

Q2
$4Na$	$2Na_2O$
$4 × 23 = 92$	$2 × [(2 × 23) + 16] = 124$
$92 ÷ 124 = 0.74$ g	$124 ÷ 124 = 1$ g
$0.74 × 2 = $ **1.5 g**	$1 × 2 = 2$ g

Q3 a) $2Al + Fe_2O_3 \rightarrow Al_2O_3 + 2Fe$

b)
Fe_2O_3	$2Fe$
$[(2 × 56) + (3 × 16)] = 160$	$2 × 56 = 112$
$160 ÷ 160 = 1$ g	$112 ÷ 160 = 0.7$
$1 × 20 = 20$ g	$0.7 × 20 = $ **14 g**

Q4 $CaCO_3 \rightarrow CaO + CO_2$
$CaCO_3$	CaO
$40 + 12 + (3 × 16) = 100$	$40 + 16 = 56$
$100 ÷ 56 = 1.786$ kg	$56 ÷ 56 = 1$ kg
$1.786 × 100 = $ **178.6 kg**	$1 × 100 = 100$ kg

Q5 a)
C	$2CO$
12	$2 × (12 + 16) = 56$
$12 ÷ 12 = 1$ g	$56 ÷ 12 = 4.67$ g
$1 × 10 = 10$ g	$4.67 × 10 = 46.7$ g

46.7 g of CO is produced in stage B — all this is used in stage C.
$3CO$	$3CO_2$
$3 × (12 + 16) = 84$	$3 × [12 + (2 × 16)] = 132$
$84 ÷ 84 = 1$ g	$132 ÷ 84 = 1.57$ g
$1 × 46.7 = 46.7$ g	$1.57 × 46.7 = $ **73.3 g**

b) It could be recycled and used in stage B.

Q6 a) $2NaOH + H_2SO_4 \rightarrow Na_2SO_4 + 2H_2O$

b)
$2NaOH$	Na_2SO_4
$2 × (23 + 16 + 1) = 80$	$(2 × 23) + 32 + (4 × 16) = 142$
$80 ÷ 142 = 0.56$ g	$142 ÷ 142 = 1$ g
$0.56 × 75 = $ **42 g**	$1 × 75 = 75$ g

c)
H_2SO_4	$2H_2O$
$(2 × 1) + 32 + (4 × 16) = 98$	$2 × [(2 × 1) + 16] = 36$
$98 ÷ 98 = 1$ g	$36 ÷ 98 = 0.37$ g
$1 × 50 = 50$ g	$0.37 × 50 = $ **18.5 g**

Page 67 — Percentage Yield and Reversible Reactions

Q1 a) yield, higher, percentage yield, predicted

b) $(6 ÷ 15) × 100 = 40\%$

c) When the solution was filtered a bit of barium sulfate may have been lost. Less product means a lower percentage yield.

d) i) Not all the reactants are turned into products because the reaction goes both ways. So the percentage yield is reduced.

ii) The unexpected reaction will use up the reactants, so there's not as much left to make the product you want. So the percentage yield is reduced.

Q2 E.g. a low yield means wasted chemicals which isn't sustainable. Increasing the yield would save resources for the future.

Page 68 — Chemical Analysis and Instrumental Methods

Q1 a) Extract the colour from the sweet by placing it in a small cup with a few drops of solvent. Put a spot of the coloured solution on a pencil baseline on filter paper.
Put the paper in a beaker of solvent (keep the baseline above the solvent). After the solvent has seeped up the paper, measure the distance the dyes have travelled. Repeat for each sweet.

b) Blue has 2 dyes.

c) Brown, because the same pattern of dyes are present.

Q2 a) E.g. they're very fast

b) E.g. they're very accurate and very sensitive/can detect even the tiniest amounts of a substance.

Q3 a) i) 2

ii) 6 and 10 minutes

b) Work out the relative molecular mass of each of the substances from the graph it draws.

Pages 69-71 — Mixed Questions — Chemistry 2a

Q1 a) i) giant covalent

ii) All the atoms are bonded to each other by strong covalent bonds so it takes a lot of energy to separate the carbon atoms.

b) i) T

ii) nanoparticle / fullerene

Q2 a)

	Silicon	Chlorine
Mass (g)	1.4	7.1
÷ A_r	$(1.4 ÷ 28) = 0.05$	$(7.1 ÷ 35.5) = 0.2$
Ratio	1	4

Empirical formula = $SiCl_4$

b) $(35.5 × 4) ÷ [(35.5 × 4) + 28] × 100 = $ **83.5%**

c) $Si + 2Cl_2 \rightarrow SiCl_4$

d)
Si	$SiCl_4$
28	$28 + (4 × 35.5) = 170$
$28 ÷ 28 = 1$ g	$170 ÷ 28 = 6.07$ g
$1 × 1.4 = 1.4$ g	$6.07 × 1.4 = $ **8.5 g**

Q3 a) Any one from: A / B / F.
Simple molecular substances have weak intermolecular forces and therefore low melting and boiling points. / They do not conduct electricity since there are no ions and so no charge.

b) C

c) All metals are good conductors of electricity when solid. / Substance D is a poor conductor of electricity when solid.

Q4 a) false

b) false

c) true

Q5 a) $24 + [2 × (14 + 16 × 3)] = 148$

b)
Mg	$Mg(NO_3)_2$
24	$24 + [2 × (14 + 16 × 3)] = 148$
$24 ÷ 24 = 1$ g	$148 ÷ 24 = 6.17$ g
$1 × 12 = 12$ g	$6.17 × 12 = $ **74 g**

c) E.g. in a reversible reaction some of the products turn back into other reactants. / Unexpected reactions can take place and use up some of the reactants. / Some liquid or solid can be lost during filtration.

Q6 a) i) ionic compound

ii) metal

iii) alloy

b) i) substance i) (ionic compound)

ii) Ionic substances don't conduct electricity when solid as the ions are not free to move.

c) $CaCl_2$

Q7 a) gas, speeds, chromatograph, compounds, retention time, identify, mass spectrometer

b) E.g. it's more accurate.

Chemistry 2b — Reaction Rates, Salts and Electrolysis

Chemistry 2b — Reaction Rates, Salts and Electrolysis

Page 72 — Rate of Reaction

Q1 a) higher
b) lower
c) decreases
d) does
Q2 a) i) Z
ii) It has the steepest gradient. / It becomes flat sooner.
b) Equal masses of marble chips were used each time.
c) The curve should be steeper and show that a larger volume of gas is produced, e.g. like this:

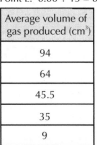

Q3 a) decrease
b) More reactant was used.
c) The reactants in Q might be in smaller pieces/have a larger surface area/be more concentrated/be at a higher temperature.

Pages 73-74 — Measuring Rates of Reaction

Q1 rate, reactants, formed, precipitation, faster, gas, mass, volume
Q2 a) C
b) i) Point K: $0.08 \div 5 = 0.016$ g/s
ii) Point L: $0.06 \div 15 = 0.004$ g/s
Q3 a)

Average volume of gas produced (cm³)
94
64
45.5
35
9

b) 50 in the third column of the table should be circled.
c) 2 mol/dm³
d) i) gas syringe
ii) Any one from: e.g. stopwatch / stopclock / timer / balance / measuring cylinder
e) Sketch should look something like this:

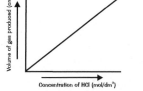

f) To improve the reliability of his results.
g) E.g. misreading the value from the gas syringe. / Not emptying the gas syringe before starting.

Pages 75-78 — Rate of Reaction Experiments

Q1 increase, faster, smaller, react
Q2 a) B

b) Curve should look something like this:

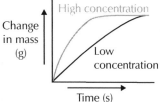

c) Size of marble pieces.
d) No, you cannot tell if it was a fair test. The same mass of marble chips was used each time but it is not known if the same volume of HCl was used each time or if the temperature was kept constant.
e) Measuring how quickly the reaction loses mass.
Q3 a) 13 (he took one at the start).
b) x-axis: time (s)
y-axis: change/loss in mass (g)
c)

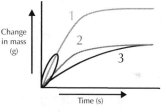

d) $145.73 - 143.89 = 1.84$ g
Q4 a) 1, because the slope of the graph is steepest.
b)

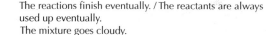

c) The reactions finish eventually. / The reactants are always used up eventually.
Q5 The mixture goes cloudy.
Q6 a) water bath, stopclock, thermometer.
b) i) faster
ii) 145 s
c) i) temperature
ii) time taken for cross to disappear
d) Repeat the investigation to get more results and find the average for each temperature.
Q7 Increasing the concentration of HCl increases the rate of reaction.
Q8 a) $2H_2O$
b) C
c) increase
Q9 a) Volume of gas (cm³/dm³/l/ml)
b) i) R
ii) Reaction R has the steepest graph and becomes flat sooner, so it is the fastest reaction and must have the most effective catalyst.

Page 79 — Collision Theory

Q1 increasing the temperature — makes the particles move faster, so they collide more often
decreasing the concentration — means fewer particles of reactant are present, so less frequent collisions occur
increasing the surface area — gives particles a bigger area of solid reactant to react with
Q2 a) energy
b) faster, more
c) rate of reaction

Chemistry 2b — Reaction Rates, Salts and Electrolysis

Q3 a) i) increase
   ii) The particles are closer together so collisions happen more frequently.
b)

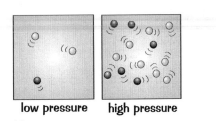

low pressure   high pressure

Q4 a) false
b) true
c) false
d) true

Page 80 — Collision Theory and Catalysts

Q1 Activation energy is the minimum amount of energy needed by particles to react.
Q2 a) A catalyst is a substance which speeds up a reaction, without being changed or used up in the reaction.
b) i) A
   ii) Reaction A has the steepest graph and becomes flat sooner so it's the fastest reaction. This means it must have used a catalyst.
Q3 a) Any one from: e.g. they allow the reaction to take place at a much lower temperature. This reduces the energy used which saves money. / They increase the rate of the reaction, so costs are reduced because the plant doesn't have to operate for as long.
b) Any two from: e.g. they can be expensive to buy. / A plant making more than one product will need more than one catalyst. / They can be poisoned by impurities and stop working.
c) E.g. the Haber process uses an iron catalyst.

Pages 81-82 — Energy Transfer in Reactions

Q1 to, heat, rise, temperature
Q2 a) N, B
b) combustion
c) E.g. adding sodium to water.
Q3 take in, heat, fall/decrease
Q4 a) thermal decomposition
b) i) endothermic
   ii) The reaction takes in heat from the surroundings.
c) i) $1\ 800\ 000 \div 1000 = 1800$ kJ
   ii) $90\ 000 \div 1\ 800\ 000 = 0.05$ tonnes or 50 kg
Q5 a) When he dropped water on it. / When it turned blue. / The second part.
b) When he heated up the copper sulphate. / The first part. / When it went white.
c) hydrated.
d) hydrated copper sulfate $\rightleftharpoons$ anhydrous copper sulfate + water
e) reversible reaction
Q6 a) X
b) N
c) X
d) N

Pages 83-84 — Acids and Alkalis

Q1 a) acid + base $\rightarrow$ **salt + water**
b) neutralisation
c) i) $H^+_{(aq)}$ and $OH^-_{(aq)}$
   ii) $H^+_{(aq)}$
   iii) $OH^-_{(aq)}$
   iv) $OH^-_{(aq)}$
   v) $H^+_{(aq)}$
Q2 a) neutral

b) E.g. universal indicator
c) 7
d) alkali
Q3 a) $HCl_{(aq)} + NaOH_{(aq)} \rightarrow \mathbf{NaCl_{(aq)} + H_2O_{(l)}}$
b) $H^+_{(aq)} + OH^-_{(aq)} \rightarrow H_2O_{(l)}$
c) an indicator (e.g. Universal indicator)
d) pH 7
Q4 a) s
b) l
c) g
d) aq
Q5 a) baking soda or soap powder
b) They are weak bases and so would neutralise the acid but wouldn't irritate or harm the skin. (Stronger bases like caustic soda might damage the skin.)
Q6 a)

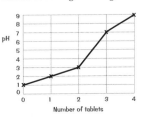

b) The pH increases from pH 1 to pH 9. (It increases most sharply between pH 3 and pH 7.)
c) 3

Pages 85-86 — Acids Reacting with Metals

Q1 a)

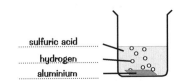

sulfuric acid
hydrogen
aluminium

b) aluminium + **sulfuric acid** $\rightarrow$ aluminium sulfate + **hydrogen**
c) $2Al + 3H_2SO_4 \rightarrow Al_2(SO_4)_3 + 3H_2$
d) zinc + sulfuric acid $\rightarrow$ zinc sulfate + hydrogen
e) $Mg + 2HCl \rightarrow MgCl_2 + H_2$
Q2 a) A
b) B
c) A: magnesium
   B: copper
   C: iron
   D: zinc
Q3 a) E.g. the number of gas bubbles produced in a certain time. / The time it takes for the metal to disappear completely. / The volume of gas produced in a certain time. / Loss of mass in a certain time.
b) acid concentration
c) Any two from: e.g. volume of acid. / Mass of the metal pieces. / Size of the metal pieces. / Temperature.
Q4 metals, hydrogen, copper, reactive, more, chloride, sulfuric, nitric
Q5 a) i) $Ca + 2HCl \rightarrow CaCl_2 + H_2$
   ii) $2Na + 2HCl \rightarrow 2NaCl + H_2$
   iii) $2Li + H_2SO_4 \rightarrow Li_2SO_4 + H_2$
b) i) magnesium bromide
   ii) $2Al + 6HBr \rightarrow 2AlBr_3 + 3H_2$

Pages 87-88 — Oxides, Hydroxides and Ammonia

Q1 a) hydrochloric acid + lead oxide $\rightarrow$ **lead** chloride + water
b) nitric acid + copper hydroxide $\rightarrow$ copper **nitrate** + water
c) sulfuric acid + zinc oxide $\rightarrow$ zinc sulfate + **water**
d) hydrochloric acid + **nickel** oxide $\rightarrow$ nickel **chloride** + **water**
e) **nitric** acid + copper oxide $\rightarrow$ **copper** nitrate + **water**
f) sulfuric acid + **sodium** hydroxide $\rightarrow$ sodium **sulfate** + **water**

Chemistry 2b — Reaction Rates, Salts and Electrolysis

Q2 a) The following should be ticked:
Acids react with metal oxides to form a salt and water.
Salts and water are formed when acids react with metal hydroxides.
Ammonia solution is alkaline.

b) $H_2SO_4 + CuO \rightarrow CuSO_4 + H_2O$
$HCl + NaOH \rightarrow NaCl + H_2O$

Q3 a) E.g. potassium oxide/hydroxide + sulfuric acid
b) ammonia + hydrochloric acid
c) E.g. silver oxide/hydroxide + nitric acid

Q4 a) NH_3
b) alkaline, nitrogen, proteins, salts, fertilisers
c) ammonia + nitric acid $\rightarrow$ ammonium nitrate
d) Because it has nitrogen from two sources, the ammonia and the nitric acid.
e) No water is produced.

Q5 a) i) $CuO_{(s)}$
ii) $H_2O_{(l)}$
iii) $HCl_{(aq)}$
iv) $ZnO_{(s)}$
v) $Na_2SO_{4(aq)} + 2H_2O_{(l)}$

b) i) $2NaOH + H_2SO_4 \rightarrow Na_2SO_4 + 2H_2O$
ii) $Mg(OH)_2 + 2HNO_3 \rightarrow Mg(NO_3)_2 + 2H_2O$
iii) $2NH_3 + H_2SO_4 \rightarrow (NH_4)_2SO_4$

Pages 89-90 — Making Salts

Q1 a) soluble
b) insoluble
c) acids, neutralised
d) precipitation

Q2 a) B
b) C
c) A

Q3 a) **silver nitrate + sodium chloride** $\rightarrow$ silver chloride + **sodium nitrate**
b) The silver chloride must be filtered out of the solution. It needs to be washed and then dried on filter paper.
c) E.g. the removal of poisonous ions from drinking water. / The removal of calcium and magnesium ions from hard water.

Q4 a) The nickel oxide will sink to the bottom of the flask.
b) i)

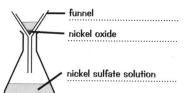

funnel
nickel oxide
nickel sulfate solution

ii) filtration
c) Evaporate some of the water (to make the solution more concentrated) and then leave the rest to evaporate very slowly.
d) nickel and nickel hydroxide
e) i) As potassium hydroxide is a soluble base, you can't tell when the reaction is finished — you can't just add an excess of solid to the acid and filter out what's left.
ii) You have to add exactly the right amount of alkali to just neutralise the acid — you need to use an indicator to show when the reaction's finished. Then repeat using exactly the same volumes of alkali and acid so the salt isn't contaminated with indicator.

Page 91 — Electrolysis

Q1 electric current, ionic, molten, elements, electrolysis, liquid, free ions, conduct, flow, positive, negative, atoms/molecules, molecules/atoms
Q2 a) It could be melted.
b) lead and bromine

c) i) true
ii) false
iii) true
iv) false
v) false

Page 92 — Electrolysis of Sodium Chloride Solution

Q1 a) The product is hydrogen unless the metal ions are less reactive than hydrogen — in which case the metal ions will form atoms.
b) hydrogen

Q2 sodium chloride, chlorine, plastics/bleach, bleach/plastics, negative electrode, sodium hydroxide, soap

Q3 a) A: H^+
B: Cl^-
C: H_2
D: Cl_2
b) Positive electrode: $2Cl^- \rightarrow Cl_2 + 2e^-$
Negative electrode: $2H^+ + 2e^- \rightarrow H_2$

Page 93 — Extraction of Aluminium and Electroplating

Q1 a) i) bauxite
ii) aluminium oxide, Al_2O_3
b) i) false
ii) true
iii) true
iv) false
v) false
c) The oxygen produced at the positive electrode reacts with the carbon in the electrode to produce carbon dioxide. So the positive electrodes gradually get 'eaten away'.

Q2 a)

positive electrode
pure silver strip
negative electrode

b) silver/Ag^+
c) E.g. to make it look attractive without the expense of making it from solid silver.
d) E.g. plating metals for electronic circuits / computers.

Pages 94-96 — Mixed Questions — Chemistry 2b

Q1 a) Increasing the temperature.
Increasing the concentration of the reactants (or the pressure if it's a gas).
Adding a catalyst.
Increasing the surface area of solid reactants.
b) The amount of product formed.

Q2 a) Q
b) R
c) Measure the volume of gas given off using a gas syringe.

Q3 a) true
b) true
c) false
d) true
e) true

Q4 a) i) acidic
ii) alkaline
b) i) neutralisation
ii) exothermic

Q5 a) $Mg + 2HCl \rightarrow MgCl_2 + H_2$
b) The pH would increase. / It would become less acidic, until it finally reached neutral/pH 7 (if there was enough magnesium).

Physics 2a — Forces and Their Effects

c)   Magnesium sulfate.

Q6 a) i)   They gain electrons to become aluminium atoms again.

     ii) $Al^{3+}_{(aq)} + 3e^- \rightarrow Al_{(s)}$

   b) $2O^{2-}_{(aq)} \rightarrow O_{2(g)} + 4e^-$

Q7   Aluminium oxide has a very high melting point. Dissolving it in molten cryolite brings the melting point down. This reduces the energy needed and makes the electrolysis cheaper.

Q8 a) i) $MgCl_2$

     ii) $MgO_{(s)} + 2HCl_{(aq)} \rightarrow MgCl_{2(aq)} + H_2O_{(l)}$

   b)   sulfuric acid/H_2SO_4

   c)   bases

Q9 a) i)   hydrogen and chlorine

     ii)   E.g. chlorine is used in the manufacture of plastics. / Chlorine is used in the manufacture of bleach.

   b)   The sodium ions stay in solution because they're more reactive than hydrogen. Hydroxide ions from water are also left behind. This means that sodium hydroxide (NaOH) is left in the solution.

   c)   Coating the surface of one metal with another metal.

Physics 2a — Forces and Their Effects

Page 97 — Velocity and Distance-Time Graphs

Q1   –12 m/s

Q2 a)   180 s (or 3 mins)

   b)   Speed = gradient of graph = distance ÷ time
Speed = 450 ÷ 180 = 2.5 m/s

   c)   He runs there in half the time it took him to walk there — 90 s. So the graph looks like this:

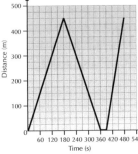

Q3   The graph shows that the motorist accelerates for about 1.5 seconds, then travels at a constant speed. So the gradient of the graph between 1.5 s and 3.0 s will give you the speed.
Gradient = vertical change ÷ horizontal change = (72 – 18) ÷ (3.0 – 1.5) = 54 ÷ 1.5 = **36 m/s** — i.e. she was exceeding the speed limit. So the motorist wasn't telling the truth.

Pages 98-99 — Acceleration and Velocity-Time Graphs

Q1 a)   The car accelerates from rest, so the change in velocity is **20 m/s**.
Acceleration = change in velocity ÷ time taken = 20 ÷ 3.5 = **5.7 m/s²**.

   b)   Change in velocity = 20 – 3 = 17 m/s.
So acceleration = 17 ÷ 2.8 = **6.1 m/s²**.
The car has a greater acceleration than before. (This assumes that the modified car's acceleration from 0 to 3 m/s is not slower.)

Q2 a)   Since the egg was dropped from rest, its change in speed is 80 m/s. So acceleration = 80 ÷ 8 = **10 m/s²**.

   b)   Now rearrange the formula to get time taken
Time taken = change in velocity ÷ acceleration = 40 ÷ 10 = **4 s**

Q3   Rearranging the formula for acceleration you get:
change in speed = acceleration × time = 2 × 4 = 8 m/s.
Change in speed = final speed – initial speed, so initial speed = final speed – change in speed = 24 – 8 = **16 m/s**.

Q4   Acceleration = gradient = 8 ÷ 5 = **1.6 m/s²**.

Q5   **A** — (constant) acceleration (from 0 - 3 m/s)
B — constant speed (of 3 m/s)
C — (constant) acceleration (from 3 - 9 m/s)
D — constant speed (of 9 m/s)
E — (constant) deceleration (from 9 - 7 m/s)

Q6   The distance the bus driver travelled before stopping is equal to the area under the graph. To find it, split the graph into a rectangle and a triangle.
Area of the rectangle = base × height = 0.75 × 12 = 9 m.
Area of the triangle = half × base × height = 0.5 × 2.5 × 12 = 15 m. Total distance = 9 m + 15 m = **24 m**.
He didn't hit the piglet.

Page 100 — Weight, Mass and Gravity

Q1   mass, kilograms, weight, newtons, gravitational

Q2 a)   W = m × g
m = 58 kg, g = 10 N/kg
W = 58 × 10 = **580 N**

   b)   Change in weight = 580 – 460 = 120 N
Change in mass = change in weight ÷ g
= 120 ÷ 10 = **12 kg**

Q3 a)   Mass is the amount of matter, which stays constant. Weight is the force of gravity on this mass, and as the gravity is a different strength on Mars her weight changes.

   b)   Mass = weight ÷ gravitational field strength, which on Earth is 10 N/kg, so the rock has a mass of 5 kg.
1.9 kg ÷ 5 kg = 0.38
The scales read 38% of the true mass, so the gravitational field strength on Mars is 38% of that on Earth. 10 N/kg × 0.38 = **3.8 N/kg** (or m/s²).

Page 101 — Resultant Forces

Q1 a)   The teapot's weight is balanced by a reaction force from the table.

   b) i)   No. The teapot is accelerating so the forces can't be balanced.

     ii)   The reaction force from the floor.

Q2 a)

     Reaction
     Drag / air resistance
     Thrust
     Weight

   b)   No — he is decelerating. South.

Q3 a)   1 500 000 – 1 500 000 = 0 N

   b)   6 000 000 – 1 500 000 = 4 500 000 N

Q4 a)   There is a resultant force — the ball is slowing down, which is deceleration.

   b)   There is a resultant force — motion in a circle means constantly changing direction, which requires acceleration.

   c)   There is no resultant force — the vase is stationary on the window ledge.

Pages 102-104 — Forces and Acceleration

Q1   balanced, stationary, constant, non-zero, accelerates, resultant force, interact, opposite

Q2   The third statement should be ticked —
The driving force of the engine is equal to friction and air resistance combined.

Q3 a)   Statement **C** should be circled — The thrust is equal to the air resistance and the lift is equal to the weight.

   b) i)   The thrust is **less than** the air resistance.

     ii)   The lift is **less than** the weight.

Physics 2a — Forces and Their Effects

Q4 Force = mass × acceleration.
Disraeli 9000: 800 kg × 5 m/s² = 4000 N
Palmerston 6i: 1560 kg × 0.7 m/s² = 1092 N
Heath TT: 950 kg × 3 m/s² = 2850 N
Asquith 380: 790 kg × 2 m/s² = 1580 N
So the correct order is: **Palmerston 6i, Asquith 380, Heath TT, Disraeli 9000.**

Q5 a) The force of the engine is 110 kg × 2.80 m/s² = **308 N.**
b) Mass = force ÷ acceleration = 308 ÷ 1.71 = **180 kg** (to 3 s.f.).

Q6 Using F = ma, the resultant force on the mass must be 1 kg × 0.25 m/s² = 0.25 N.
Resultant force = force on the newton-meter – force of friction (they act in opposite directions).
0.25 N = 0.4 N – force of friction, so force of friction = 0.4 N – 0.25 N = **0.15 N.**

Q7 The third statement should be ticked — The car's pulling force accelerates the caravan. The caravan's reaction acts on the car, not the caravan.

Q8 The first statement should be ticked — Your feet push backwards on the ground, so the ground pushes you forwards.

Q9 a) i) The van is travelling at a steady speed, so the resultant force must be 0. So the force exerted by the engine must be equal to the air resistance and friction combined.
2000 N + 500 N = **2500 N.**

ii)

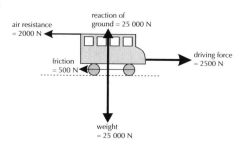

air resistance = 2000 N
reaction of ground = 25 000 N
friction = 500 N
driving force = 2500 N
weight = 25 000 N

b) The resultant force will now be 200 N (forces were previously balanced)
a = F/m = 200 ÷ 2500 = **0.08 m/s².**

c) The resultant force is now maximum driving force – (force of wind + friction + air resistance) = 2650 – 2700 = –50 N. This force acts in the opposite direction to the van's movement, so the van will continue to decelerate, but at a slower rate (0.02 m/s²).

Pages 105-106 — Frictional Force and Terminal Velocity

Q1 greater, accelerates, increase, balances, constant, greater, decelerates, decrease, balances, constant.

Q2 All the boxes except 'carrying less cargo' should be ticked.

Q3 a) Paola is **wrong** because although gravity (the accelerating force per unit mass) is the same for both objects, air resistance will affect them differently because they have different shapes.

b) Guiseppe is **right** because drag will be greater for the feather compared to its weight, so drag will balance its weight sooner. The hammer will continue to accelerate for longer than the feather.

Q4 No, Mavis can't draw any conclusions.
The terminal velocity depends not only on drag (which is determined by the size, shape and smoothness of the object) but on the weight of the object, and the weights of the balls will be different.

Q5 Region A: weight is greater
Region B: both equal
Region C: air resistance is greater
Region D: both equal

Q6 a) No, Kate isn't really moving upwards. She only **seems** to move upwards when she opens her parachute because she slows down relative to the camera (which is held by Alison — who hasn't opened her parachute yet).

b) She decelerates until she reaches her terminal velocity and then falls at this speed until she lands.

Q7 a) Venus's atmosphere is much thicker than Earth's so a parachute the same size or smaller would provide enough drag to slow the probe to a safe speed.

b) Mars has lower gravity, so less drag is required to balance the probe's weight, but there is much less resistance from the thinner atmosphere, so the parachute would have to be larger than one used on Earth.

Page 107 — Stopping Distances

Q1 a) The distance the car travels under the braking force before it comes to a stop.

b) The distance the car travels during the driver's reaction time.

Q2

Thinking Distance	Braking Distance
tiredness	road surface
alcohol	tyres
speed	weather
drugs	brakes
	speed
	load

Q3 The total stopping distance will increase.
Both thinking and braking distance will increase.

Q4 The friction between the brake discs and pads will be reduced if they are covered in water. This means the braking force will be reduced and the car will take longer to stop (i.e. the braking distance increases).

Q5 E.g. distractions like mobile phones won't affect Sam's thinking distance, as thinking distance is the distance travelled between the driver first spotting a hazard and taking action. However, it will mean that she will be less likely to notice a hazard until she is much closer to it. (So she is much more likely to crash if there is a hazard.)

Pages 108-109 — Work and Potential Energy

Q1 a) Work done and energy transferred are the same thing, so Jenny does **50 J** of work.

b) Distance = work done ÷ force = 50 ÷ 250 = **0.2 m**

Q2 To push your bicycle you need to apply a force to overcome resistant forces like friction. The work done is equal to the force you apply (in the direction of motion) multiplied by the distance you push your bike.

Q3 a) True
b) False
c) True
d) True
e) False ($E_p = m \times g \times h = 3 \times 10 \times 2.5 = $ **75 J**)

Q4 a) $E_p = m \times g \times h = 25$ kg × 10 N/kg × 1.2 m = **300 J.**
b) Total $E_p = 28 \times 300$ J = **8400 J.**
c) The energy transferred and the work done by Dave are the same thing, so **8400 J.**

Q5 a) Distance = work done ÷ force = 80 000 ÷ 50 N = **1600 m**
b) i) Work = force × distance,
so force = work ÷ distance = 90 000 ÷ 120 = **750 N.**
weight / gravity
ii) Work = gravitational potential energy = mass × g × height,
so mass = work ÷ (g × height)
mass = 90 000 ÷ (10 × 120) = **75 kg**
(OR: Weight = mass × g
so mass = weight ÷ g = 750 ÷ 10 = **75 kg**)

Q6 a) Rearrange E_p = mass × g × height:
height = E_p ÷ (m × g) = 4000 ÷ (50 × 10) = 8 m
b) The energy converted from potential energy to kinetic energy is 1500 J, so the difference must be the wasted energy. 4000 J – 1500 J = **2500 J.**
c) friction
d) Force = work ÷ distance = 2500 ÷ 50 = **50 N**
e) Energy wasted = 4000 J – 2000 J = **2000 J.**
Force = 2000 ÷ 50 = **40 N**

Physics 2a — Forces and Their Effects

f) The mat reduces the amount of friction. Less energy is wasted and so more potential energy is converted into kinetic energy.

g) Force = 2000 ÷ 5 = **400 N**

Page 110 — Kinetic Energy

Q1 a) true
b) false
c) true

Q2 a) Just before the ball hits the ground, it has converted all of its potential energy into kinetic energy, so it has **242 J** of kinetic energy.

b)
$$v = \sqrt{\frac{2 \times E_k}{m}} = \sqrt{\frac{2 \times 242}{0.1}} = 69.6 \text{ m/s}$$

Q3 a) i)
$$v = \sqrt{\frac{2 \times E_k}{m}} = \sqrt{\frac{2 \times 614\,400}{1200}} = 32 \text{ m/s}$$

ii)
$$v = \sqrt{\frac{2 \times E_k}{m}} = \sqrt{\frac{2 \times 614\,400}{12\,288}} = 10 \text{ m/s}$$

b) The **car** has more kinetic energy — doubling speed increases K.E. by a factor of 4 whereas trebling mass only increases K.E. by a factor of 3.

Q4 a) Distance = work done by brakes / force
= 1440 ÷ 200 = **7.2 m**.

b) The temperature of the brakes increases because the kinetic energy of the wheels is transferred to the heat energy of the brakes.

Page 111 — Forces and Elasticity

Q1 a) E.g. if something is elastic it means that when a force is applied it changes its shape and stores the work as elastic potential energy. When the force is removed the elastic object can return to its original shape.

b) The kinetic energy is transferred into the elastic potential energy of the springs around the trampoline as they stretch (as well as a bit of heat and sound energy).

c) i) 600 ÷ 30 = **20 N** per spring
ii) F = k × e
Rearranging gives: k = F ÷ e = 20 ÷ 0.1 = **200 N/m**.

Q2 a) F = k × e
F = 45 × 15 = **675 N**

b) i) The limit of proportionality.
ii) No, once an elastic object is extended beyond its limit of proportionality it will be permanently stretched and won't extend proportionally with force.

Pages 112-113 — Power

Q1 rate, energy, watts, joules, one hundred, light/ heat, heat/light

Q2 a) Power = energy ÷ time, P = E ÷ t
(Or equivalent, e.g. E = P × t.)

b) Rearrange the formula to get energy = power × time. The car gets 50 000 × 5 × 60 = **15 000 000 J** of energy (= 15 000 kJ / 15 MJ).

c) Power = energy transferred ÷ time taken
= 144 000 ÷ (12 × 60) = **200 W**

Q3 Gravitational potential energy = mass × g × height.
a) i) 46 × 10 × 5 = **2300 J**.
ii) 48 × 10 × 5 = **2400 J**.

b) Power = work done ÷ time
Catherine's power = 2300 ÷ 6.2 = **371 W**.
Sally's power = 2400 ÷ 6.4 = **375 W**.
Sally generated more power.

Q4 a) Time in seconds = 10 × 60 = 600 s.
Energy = power × time = 150 × 600 = **90 000 J** (= 90 kJ).

b) 90 kJ ÷ 30 kJ/ml = **3 ml**.

c) Power = energy ÷ time = 120 000 ÷ (10 × 60) = **200 W**

Q5 a) Josie is carrying her school bag so her total mass is 66 kg. The energy transferred by Josie is the kinetic energy she gains from her acceleration.
K.E = ½ × m × v² = 0.5 × 66 × 8² = 2112 J
Power = energy transferred ÷ time taken
= 2112 ÷ 6 = **352 W**

b) Josie puts down her school bag so her total mass is now only 60 kg. This time the energy is the gravitational potential energy she gains going up the stairs.
E_p = m × g × h = 60 × 10 × 5 = 3000 J
P = E ÷ t = 3000 J ÷ 4 = **750 W**

Q6 a) Start 4 – this wasn't a fair test because he slipped.

b) Remembering to ignore start 4 —
average time = **3.2 s**, average speed = **8.0 m/s**.

c) E.g. calculate the power for each start, e.g. for sprint 1 power = (1/2 × 70 × 8²) / 3.2 = 700 W.
Then average these powers. 2804 ÷ 4 = **701 W**.

Page 114 — Momentum and Collisions

Q1 a) If the velocity of a moving object doubles, its **momentum** will double.

b) If you drop a suitcase out of a moving car, the car's momentum will **decrease**.

c) When two objects collide the total momentum **stays the same**.

d) When a force acts on an object its momentum **changes**.

Q2 Truck A's momentum = 30 m/s × 3000 kg
= 90 000 kg m/s.
Truck B's momentum = 10 m/s × 4500 kg
= 45 000 kg m/s.
Truck C's momentum = 20 m/s × 4000 kg
= 80 000 kg m/s.
Truck D's momentum = 15 m/s × 3500 kg
= 52 500 kg m/s.
So the order of increasing momentum is: **B, D, C, A**.

Q3 a)

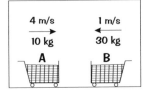

b) **Before** the collision:
Trolley A's momentum = 10 kg × 4 m/s = 40 kg m/s.
Trolley B's momentum = 30 kg × (−1 m/s) = −30 kg m/s.
(Note the minus sign for trolley B's velocity because it's travelling in the opposite direction to trolley A.)
So total momentum = 40 + (−30) = 10 kg m/s.
After the collision:
The joined trolleys have mass 40 kg and velocity v.
Momentum$_{before}$ = momentum$_{after}$ = 10 kg m/s = 40 kg × v
So, v = 10 kg m/s ÷ 40 kg = **+0.25 m/s**.
The '+' sign shows that the joined trolleys travel in the same direction that trolley A was originally moving (i.e. east).

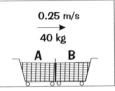

Pages 115-116 — Car Design and Safety

Q1 work, heat, regenerative, reverse, electric generator, chemical, efficient

Q2 a) Kinetic energy.

b) The brakes convert the kinetic energy into other forms of energy — mostly heat energy.

Q3 E.g. a roof box will make the car less aerodynamic and will increase the air resistance. The air resistance will therefore equal the driving force at lower speeds and the top speed will be reduced.

Q4 a) E.g. by slowing the car and passengers down over a longer period of time, you spread out the change in momentum and reduce the force that the passengers experience. OR: you decrease the size of the deceleration. This reduces the forces on the car and passengers (F = ma), leading to less severe injuries for the passengers.

b) E.g. any two from:
Crumple zones – these crumple in a collision and convert some of the car's kinetic energy into heat and sound energy as it changes shape.
Side impact bars – these direct the kinetic energy of a crash away from the passengers and towards other parts of the car, such as the crumple zones.
Airbags – transfer part of the passenger's kinetic energy to the gas inside the airbag which escapes through pores in the material. (They also prevent the passenger from hitting hard surfaces within the car.)

Q5 a) A seat belt absorbs kinetic energy as the material of the belt stretches.

b) When a car crashes it changes velocity very suddenly. This means that there is a large momentum change which can mean a very large force on the passenger. By slowing down that change in momentum, the seat belt reduces the force on the internal organs, reducing the likelihood of injury.

Q6 Convert time in hours to time in seconds:
1 hour = 60 mins = 60×60 s = 3600 s
$P = E \div t = 2\,650\,000\,000 \div 3600 = \mathbf{736\,111\,W} = (736\,kW)$

Pages 117-119 — Mixed Questions — Physics 2a

Q1 a) Work done = force × distance = 300×1500 = **450 000 J** (or 450 kJ).

b) Acceleration = change in speed ÷ time taken = $20 \div 6.2 = \mathbf{3.23\,m/s^2}$ (to 3 s.f.).

c) This will reduce the top speed of the car — the air resistance against the car will be increased, and so will equal the maximum driving force at a lower speed.

d) A seat belt will increase the time over which there is a momentum change, so he will experience a smaller force.

e) E.g. the crumple zones increase the time over which Mr Alsono and his car change momentum in the crash, which decreases the force he experiences.

Q2 a) $W = m \times g = 1200 \times 10 = \mathbf{12\,000\,N}$.

b) $E_p = m \times g \times h = 12\,000 \times 34 = \mathbf{408\,000\,J}$ (= 408 kJ).

c) Two thirds of the potential energy is converted into kinetic energy, so gain in E_k = $408\,000 \times 2/3$ = 272 000 J. Two thirds of the way down, speed =
$$v = \sqrt{\frac{2 \times E_k}{m}} = \sqrt{\frac{2 \times 272\,000}{1200}} = \mathbf{21.3\,m/s}\ (3\ s.f.)$$

d) Time = speed ÷ acceleration = $20 \div 6.4 = \mathbf{3.125\,s}$.

Q3 a) $120\,s - 60\,s = \mathbf{60\,s}$ (1 minute).

b) Both lines are straight (initially).

c) Train 1 is faster.
Speed = gradient = $50 \div 40 = \mathbf{1.25\,m/s}$.

d) E.g. train 1 is decelerating / has a negative acceleration / is slowing down.

Q4 a) No — the car is not changing speed or direction / not accelerating and so there cannot be a resultant force.

b) 90 km/h = $90\,000 \div 3600$ = 25 m/s.
momentum = $m \times v = 2100 \times 25 = \mathbf{52\,500\,kg\,m/s}$

c) i) E.g. any two of: how tired she is / how fast she is driving / whether she had consumed alcohol / whether she had consumed drugs etc.

ii) F = change in momentum ÷ time = $52\,500 \div 3.0 = \mathbf{17\,500\,N}$

Q5 a) As soon as it's dropped the dummy accelerates under the influence of gravity. So as it falls its velocity increases steadily. When it hits the ground its velocity changes almost instantly to zero and stays at zero.

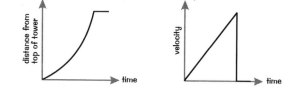

b) i) Work done = potential energy gained
= $m \times g \times h = 95 \times 10 \times 60 = \mathbf{57\,000\,J}$ (or 57 kJ).

ii) Time = work ÷ power = $57\,000 \div 760 = \mathbf{75\,s}$.

c) Weight of dummy = $m \times g = 95 \times 10 = 950$ N
$k = F \div e = 950 \div 5 = \mathbf{190\,N/m}$

Q6 a) her weight / gravity

b) 700 N

c) There is now a resultant force on her, acting upwards. This accelerates her upwards, reducing her downward velocity.

d) 700 N

Physics 2b — Electricity and the Atom

Page 120 — Static Electricity

Q1 Circled: positive and negative, negative and positive.
Underlined: negative and negative, positive and positive.

Q2 static, insulating, friction, electrons, positive / negative, negative / positive

Q3 a) A polythene rod becomes negatively charged when rubbed with a duster because it **gains** electrons.

b) When a negatively charged object and a positively charged object are brought together, **both** the **objects exert** a force **on each other**.

c) The closer two charged objects are together, the **more** strongly they attract or repel.

d) Electrical charges **can** move very easily through metals.

Q4 Electrons are transferred between the jumper and his hair, leaving his hair electrically charged. Because all the strands of hair have the same charge they repel one another — and stand on end.

Page 121 — Current and Potential Difference

Q1 charge, voltage, work, reduces, decrease

Q2 A — Current — amps
V — Potential Difference — volts
Ω — Resistance — ohms

Q3 a) $Q = I \times t$
$t = 20 \times 60 = 1200$ seconds
$5 \times 1200 = \mathbf{6000\,C}$

b) $W = V \times Q$
$3 \times 6000 = \mathbf{18\,000\,J}$ (or 18 kJ)

Q4

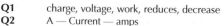

	Lamp A	Lamp B
Current through lamp (A)	2	4
Voltage drop across lamp (V)	3	2
Charge passing in 10 s (C)	20	40
Work done in 10 s (J)	60	80

Q5 a) $Q = I \times t$
$4 \times (7 \times 60) = \mathbf{1680\,C}$

b) $W = V \times Q$
$9 \times 1680 = \mathbf{15\,120\,J}$ (or **15.12 kJ**)

Physics 2b — Electricity and the Atom

Page 122 — Circuits — The Basics

Q1
Cell — Provides the 'push' on the charge.

Variable Resistor — Used to alter the current.

Component — The item you're testing.

Voltmeter — Measures the voltage.

Ammeter — Measures the current.

Q2 circuit, through, across

Q3 a) 1. Battery
2. Thermistor
3. Component / Fixed resistor
4. LDR
5. Switch (closed)
6. Filament Lamp

b) The ammeter must be drawn in series between the battery and the first junction.

c) The voltmeter must be drawn in parallel around the lamp.

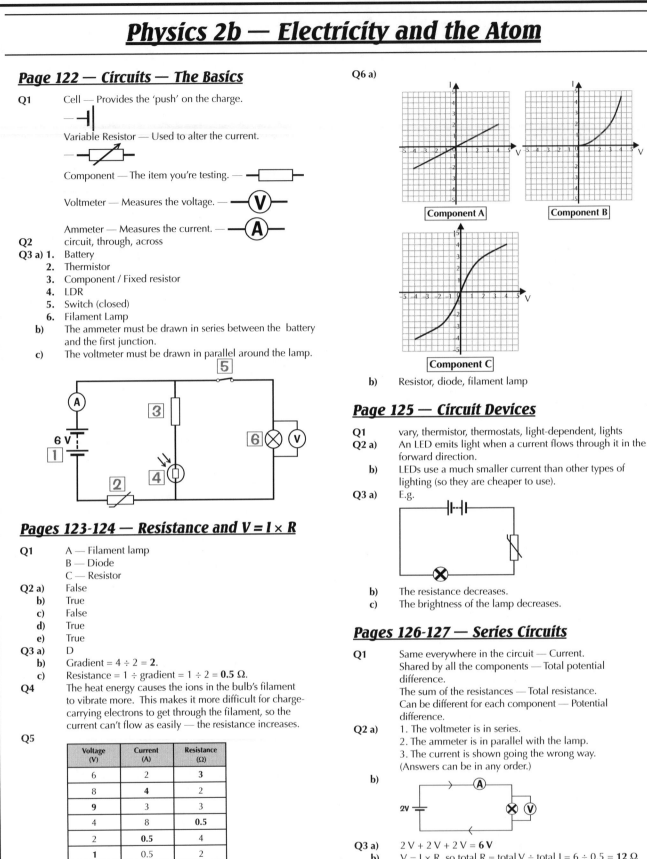

Pages 123-124 — Resistance and V = I × R

Q1 A — Filament lamp
B — Diode
C — Resistor

Q2 a) False
b) True
c) False
d) True
e) True

Q3 a) D
b) Gradient = 4 ÷ 2 = **2**.
c) Resistance = 1 ÷ gradient = 1 ÷ 2 = **0.5 Ω**.

Q4 The heat energy causes the ions in the bulb's filament to vibrate more. This makes it more difficult for charge-carrying electrons to get through the filament, so the current can't flow as easily — the resistance increases.

Q5

Voltage (V)	Current (A)	Resistance (Ω)
6	2	**3**
8	**4**	2
9	3	3
4	8	**0.5**
2	**0.5**	4
1	0.5	2

Q6 a)

Component A

Component B

Component C

b) Resistor, diode, filament lamp

Page 125 — Circuit Devices

Q1 vary, thermistor, thermostats, light-dependent, lights

Q2 a) An LED emits light when a current flows through it in the forward direction.

b) LEDs use a much smaller current than other types of lighting (so they are cheaper to use).

Q3 a) E.g.

b) The resistance decreases.

c) The brightness of the lamp decreases.

Pages 126-127 — Series Circuits

Q1 Same everywhere in the circuit — Current.
Shared by all the components — Total potential difference.
The sum of the resistances — Total resistance.
Can be different for each component — Potential difference.

Q2 a) 1. The voltmeter is in series.
2. The ammeter is in parallel with the lamp.
3. The current is shown going the wrong way.
(Answers can be in any order.)

b)

Q3 a) 2 V + 2 V + 2 V = **6 V**
b) V = I × R, so total R = total V ÷ total I = 6 ÷ 0.5 = **12 Ω**
c) R_3 = total resistance − R_1 − R_2 = 12 − 2 − 4 = **6 Ω**
d) V = I × R = 0.5 × 4 = **2 V**

Q4 a) The lamps get dimmer as more are added because the voltage is shared out between the lamps.

b) The current gets smaller as more lamps are added. Each lamp adds more resistance which means less current.

Q5 a) E.g.

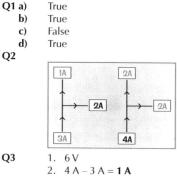

b) It decreases
c) Total resistance = resistance from resistor + resistance from motor = $1\Omega + 2\Omega = 3\Omega$.
$V = I \times R$, so $I = V \div R = 6 \div 3 = \mathbf{2A}$.

Pages 128-129 — Parallel Circuits

Q1 a) True
b) True
c) False
d) True
Q2

Q3 1. 6 V
2. $4A - 3A = \mathbf{1A}$
3. 6 V
Q4 a) Nothing, because each lamp gets its voltage from the battery separately.
b) It increases because the currents to each lamp add up.
c) Nothing happens to the brightness of the other lamps.
(The answers above assume that the internal resistance of the cell is ignored — in practice the current would decrease a little as lamps were added.)
Q5 a) E.g. no, you can have a different current in each branch, but the voltage is always the same.
b) E.g. so that the lights can be switched on and off independently. / So that if one light fails, the others will still light up.

Pages 130-131 — Series and Parallel Circuits — Examples

Q1 Series Circuits
end to end
the same everywhere
shared between components
e.g. Christmas tree lights
Parallel Circuits
side by side
can be different in each branch
the same for each component
e.g. car electrics, household electrics (or any other sensible answer)
Q2 a) If they were wired in parallel, the bulbs would be 230 V because each one would get the full voltage.
b) They don't all go off if one fails / you can tell which one has failed.
c) The bulbs will be designed to work at different voltages. In parallel 230 V bulbs are needed (although in practice transformers are often used to lower the voltage). In series the bulbs used are suitable for smaller voltages e.g. 12 V because the voltage is shared.
Q3 $V_0 = \mathbf{12V}$, $A_1 = \mathbf{1A}$, $V_1 = I \times R = 1 \times 4 = \mathbf{4V}$,
$V_3 = 12V - 4V - 2V = \mathbf{6V}$
Q4 a) i) $I = V \div R = 12 \div 2 = \mathbf{6A}$
ii) $I = V \div R = 12 \div 4 = \mathbf{3A}$
b) i) **12 V**
ii) **12 V**
c) $A_0 = A_2 + A_3 = 3A + 2A = \mathbf{5A}$

Q5 1. If the engine isn't running the battery might not be able to provide enough current for the fan and lights together at full voltage. So the lights might be slightly dimmer.
2. If the bulbs are in series, taking one out will break the circuit and all the bulbs will go out.
3. The wall lamps are in parallel but they share the same switch.

Page 132 — Mains Electricity

Q1 volts, alternating, a.c., direction, changing, frequency, hertz, batteries, direct, d.c., same
Q2 a) C
b) B
c) A
Q3 a) 2 volts
b) 4×10 ms = **40 ms** or **0.04 s**
c) Frequency = $1 \div 0.04 = \mathbf{25\ Hz}$

Page 133 — Electricity in the Home

Q1 There should be rings round: cable over cooker, overloaded socket, cable over sink, sockets too near the sink, long cable on the floor, hamster chewing the cable, child sitting on worktop sticking a fork in the socket, lamp that could easily be knocked over.
Q2 a) Because these materials are electrical insulators.
b) These materials are electrical conductors, and are used for those parts that the electricity goes through.
c) Rubber or plastic because they are electrical insulators and are flexible.
Q3 a) insulation
b) live
c) neutral
d) green and yellow, earth
e) firmly, bare
f) outer
Q4 1. The earth wire isn't connected.
2. Bare wires are showing.
3. The neutral and live wires are the wrong way round.

Page 134 — Fuses and Earthing

Q1 The live and neutral wires should normally carry the same current.
A circuit breaker does the same job as a fuse.
A Residual Current Circuit Breaker can be used instead of a fuse and earth wire.
Any metal casing should be connected to the earth wire.
A fuse melts when the current in a fuse wire exceeds the rating of the fuse.
Q2 1. A fault allows the live wire to touch the metal case.
2. A big current flows out through the earth wire.
3. A big surge in current blows the fuse.
4. The device is isolated from the live wire.
Q3 a) When an RCCB detects a difference in the current between the live and neutral wires it turns off the power by opening a switch.
b) E.g. any two from: They work much faster than fuses. / They work even for small current changes that might not be large enough to melt a fuse. / They can easily be reset whereas fuses need to be replaced once used.
Q4 a) **2 A.** (It's nearest to the actual current but still higher so that it won't blow with normal use.)
b) Because it has an insulated case with no metal parts showing.
c) two-core cable
d) They both increase with current size — the bigger the current, the higher the fuse rating needs to be and the thicker the cable needs to be to carry it.

Physics 2b — Electricity and the Atom

Page 135 — Energy and Power in Circuits

Q1 how long, power, energy, time, heat, more
Q2 a) E.g. most of the energy is wasted as heat.
b) E.g. it's more energy efficient (so cheaper to run).
c) E.g. he might think it is more cost effective to buy a cheaper bulb even though the running costs will be more (he may not plan on using the light bulb very much).
Q3 a) 1000 J, light, heat
b) 60 000 J, kinetic, heat, sound
c) 20 000 J, heat
d) 1 200 000 J, heat

Page 136 — Power and Energy Change

Q1 a)

	Lamp A	Lamp B	Lamp C
Voltage (V)	12	3	230
Current (A)	2.5	4	0.1
Power (W)	30	12	23
Energy used in one minute (J)	1800	720	1380

b) A = 3 A, B = 5 A, C = 1 A.
Q2 a) Current = power ÷ voltage = 1500 ÷ 230 = 6.5 A
b) 7 A
Q3

	Drill A	Drill B
Current through drill (A)	2	3
Voltage drop across drill (V)	230	230
Charge passing in 5 s (C)	10	15
Energy transformed in 5 s (J)	2300	3450

Q4 a) $Q = I \times t$
$0.6 \times (12 \times 60) = \textbf{432 C}$
b) $W = V \times Q$
$2 \times 432 = \textbf{864 J}$

Page 137 — Atomic Structure

Q1 a) no
b) ion
c) protons, electrons (in either order)
d) positively
Q2

Particle	Mass	Charge
Proton	1	+1
Neutron	1	0
Electron	very small	−1

Q3 a) i) They fired a beam of alpha particles at thin gold foil.
ii) They expected the positively charged alpha particles to be slightly deflected by the electrons in the plum pudding model.
b) Most of the alpha particles went straight through the foil, but the odd one came straight back at them. This showed that atoms are not like a plum pudding, they have a very small central nucleus with electrons orbiting round it. Most of the atom is empty space — the nucleus is tiny compared to the size of the atom.

Page 138 — Atoms and Radiation

Q1 a) False
b) True
c) False
d) False
e) True
Q2 a) i) Background radiation.
ii) E.g. any two from: Nuclear weapon tests. / Nuclear accidents. / Dumped nuclear waste.

b) i) Background radiation is higher in Cornwall due to the type of rock underground.
ii) E.g. any one from: food / cosmic rays / building materials.
iii) Yes. $(1000 \times 0.00001) + 0.008 = 0.018$.

Pages 139 — Ionising Radiation

Q1 Alpha particle — 2 neutrons and 2 protons — the same as a helium nucleus.
Beta particle — An electron from the nucleus.
Gamma radiation — A type of electromagnetic radiation.

Q2

Radiation Type	Ionising power weak/moderate/strong	Charge positive/none/negative	Relative mass no mass/small/large	Penetrating power low/moderate/high	Range in air short/long/very long
alpha	strong	positive	large	low	short
beta	moderate	negative	small	moderate	long
gamma	weak	none	no mass	high	very long

Q3 a) $^{234}_{90}\text{Th} \rightarrow \,^{234}_{91}\text{Pa} + \,^{0}_{-1}\text{e}$
b) $^{222}_{86}\text{Rn} \rightarrow \,^{218}_{84}\text{Po} + \,^{4}_{2}\alpha$
Q4 1. The particles move in opposite directions — this is because they have opposite charges.
2. The alpha particle is deflected less than the beta particle — this is because alpha particles have a much greater mass than beta particles.

Page 140 — Half-Life

Q1 In 60 years' time, the count rate will be half what it is now.
Q2 a) In 29 years time, the count rate will have halved — half of the radioactive nuclei will have decayed.
b) **125** (87 years is 3 half-lives.)
Q3 After 1 half-life: 720 cpm
After 2 half-lives: 360 cpm
After 3 half-lives: 180 cpm
After 4 half-lives: 90 cpm
After 5 half-lives: 45 cpm
Therefore 5 hours is 5 half-lives.
So 1 half-life = **1 hour**.
Q4 a)

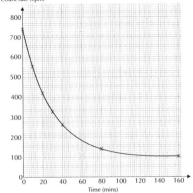

b) There will always be some background radiation (in this case it looks like approx. 100 cpm) AND the radioactivity of the sample will never fall to zero.
c) The background radiation must be subtracted from her readings. The count therefore starts at 640. Half of that is 320 (or 420 including background radiation). This occurs on the 20th minute.

Page 141 — Uses of Radiation

Q1 1. The radioactive source emits alpha particles.
2. The air between the electrodes is ionised by the alpha particles.
3. A current flows between the electrodes — the alarm stays off.

Physics 2b — Electricity and the Atom

4. A fire starts and smoke particles absorb the alpha radiation.

5. The circuit is broken so no current flows.

6. The alarm sounds.

Q2 a) A gamma-emitter with a long half-life is used. Gamma radiation is needed because it is not stopped by air or metal parts of the instruments and can kill the cells of living organisms (e.g. bacteria) on the instruments. A long half-life is needed because the sterilising machine will be in use over many years and replacing the source frequently would be inconvenient.

b) Lead is used to prevent the operator and anyone near the machine from getting too high a dose of radiation.

Q3 a) Technetium-99. It has the shortest half-life.

b) Cobalt-60. It emits gamma radiation, which can penetrate the body and can kill cancer cells. It has a fairly long half-life so the hospital would not need to replace the source too often.

Page 142 — Radioactivity Safety

Q1 a) E.g. he isn't wearing protective gloves. He isn't using tongs to handle the sample. He is pointing the sample directly into the face of the other scientist.

b) E.g. by minimising the time the samples are out of their boxes.

c) In a thick-walled, lead-lined container.

Q2 a) beta and gamma

b) i) alpha radiation

ii) It's highly ionising and can damage or kill cells in our bodies. A high dose can kill lots of cells at once, causing radiation sickness. It can also cause cancer when cells are damaged, mutate and divide uncontrollably.

Page 143 — Nuclear Fission and Fusion

Q1 uranium-235, split, heat, water, steam, turbine, generator, electricity

Q2 E.g. the slow-moving neutron is absorbed by a plutonium nucleus. This plutonium nucleus splits up, forming new lighter elements and spitting out two or three neutrons. One or more of these 'extra' neutrons may then be absorbed by another plutonium nucleus, causing it to split and spit out more neutrons, which may cause other nuclei to split etc.

Q3 E.g. any four from: Fission splits nuclei up, fusion combines nuclei. / Fission reactors use uranium or plutonium, fusion reactors use hydrogen. / Fission produces radioactive waste, fusion produces very little radioactive waste. / Fission reactors already exist, fusion reactors are still being developed. / Fusion requires extremely high temperatures, fission does not.

Q4 **Good points**
E.g. fuel is cheap and plentiful, they produce very little radioactive waste.
Bad points
E.g. no materials can stand the high temperatures needed, it requires a lot of energy to achieve such high temperatures.

Pages 144-145 — The Life Cycle of Stars

Q1 hot, fusion, stable, outwards, inwards, billions

Q2 a) Gravitational attraction pulls the material together.

b) Gas and dust in orbit around a newly formed star may clump together to form masses. The smaller masses are attracted to larger masses, and they eventually merge together to become planets.

Q3 a) A star becomes a red giant when the hydrogen fuel in its core begins to run out. (Hydrogen outside the core is burnt, heating the outer layers and causing the star to expand.)

b) It becomes red because its surface cools.

c) They cool and contract into a white dwarf and then when the light fades completely they become a black dwarf.

Q4 The explosion is called a supernova. The outer layers of dust and gas are thrown out into the universe. This leaves

a very dense core known as a neutron star. If the star is big enough this can become a black hole.

Q5 A Clouds of Dust and Gas   B Protostar
C Main Sequence Star   D Red Giant
E White Dwarf   F Black Dwarf
G Red Super Giant   H Supernova
I Neutron Star   J Black Hole

Q6 a) New elements have been formed by fusion in stars.

b) They consume massive amounts of hydrogen.

c) They are formed when a big star explodes in a supernova and are ejected into the universe.

Pages 146-148 — Mixed Questions — Physics 2b

Q1 a) The nucleus of cobalt-60 contains one more neutron than that of cobalt-59.

b) medical tracers — technetium-99m
smoke detectors — americium-241
detecting leaks in pipes — technetium-99m or cobalt-60

c) i) gamma

ii) Because the radiation damages healthy normal cells as well as the cancerous ones.

d) Work out how many half-lives would be needed.
$120 \div 2^5 = 3.75$, so just under 5 half-lives would be needed to bring the count rate down to 4 cpm.
The half-life of americium-241 is 432 years.
$432 \times 5 = 2160$. So roughly **2000 years** would be needed.

e) E.g. always handle the source with tongs. / Never allow the source to touch his skin. / Hold the source as far away from his body as possible. / Keep the source pointing away from his body. / Avoid looking directly at the source. / Store the source in a lead-lined box and put it away as soon as his experiment is finished.

Q2 a) $10 + 5 + 5 = $ **20 Ω**.

b) i) $I = V \div R = 4 \div 10 = $ **0.4 A** (current through 10 Ω resistor is the same as current in all parts of the circuit).

ii) $V = I \times R = 0.4 \times 20 = $ **8 V**.

iii) Voltage across 5 Ω resistor $= I \times R = 0.4 \times 5 = 2$ V
$P = V \times I = 2 \times 0.4 = 0.8$ W
Energy $= P \times t = 0.8 \times (2 \times 60) = $ **96 J**.

Q3 a) nuclear fission

b) A neutron hits a uranium nucleus and is absorbed, giving the nucleus too many neutrons to be stable. It then decays into two smaller nuclei and some fast-moving neutrons, which go on to cause other uranium nuclei to undergo fission.

c) The heat from the reactor is used to make steam, which turns a turbine attached to a generator, which produces the electricity.

d) E.g. doesn't produce radioactive waste, there's plenty of hydrogen around to use as fuel.

e) At the moment it takes more power to create the right conditions in a reactor needed for fusion (e.g. high temperature) than the reactor can produce.

f) i) Stars consume huge amounts of hydrogen in nuclear fusion (which creates new elements).

ii) Heat created by nuclear fusion provides an outward pressure to balance the force of gravity pulling everything inwards.

Q4 a) i) $4 \times 0.5 = $ **2.0 A**.

ii) 0 A

iii) $(4 \times 0.5) + (2 \times 6.0) = $ **14.0 A**.

b) Thermistor — they are a temperature dependent resistor. The resistance of a thermistor decreases as temperature increases and increases as temperature decreases.

c) Time period $= 10$ ms $\times 3.5 = 0.01 \times 3.5 = 0.035$ s
Frequency $= 1 \div 0.035 = $ **29 Hz**.

Q5 a) A large current flows through the live wire, passes through the metal case and out down the earth wire. The large current causes the fuse to melt, which cuts off the live supply.

b) i) live, neutral

ii) It doesn't need an earth wire because the case is made of plastic and there are no metal parts exposed or which could touch the case.

ISBN 978 1 84762 761 2

9 781847 627612

SQHA44